Lee Canter's

Assertive Discipline®
Middle School Workbook

Grades 6-8

A Publication of Lee Canter & Associates

Staff Writer
Marcia Shank

Editorial Staff
Marlene Canter
Jacqui Hook
Patricia Sarka
Kathy Winberry

Design
Bob Winberry

Illustrations
Jane Yamada
Patty Briles

©1992 Lee Canter & Associates
P.O. Box 2113, Santa Monica, CA 90407-2113
800-262-4347 310-395-3221

Printed in the United States of America
First printing June 1992

96 95 94   11 10 9 8 7 6 5 4

ISBN 0-939007-49-5

Contents

Introduction

Lee Canter's Assertive Discipline has been a highly regarded classroom behavior management program for over 15 years. In 1992 the program was revised to more comprehensively meet the needs of today's classrooms. The focus of the new Assertive Discipline is on teaching students responsible behavior. With this proactive and preventive approach, teachers can go beyond establishing basic discipline in their classrooms to creating learning environments in which students learn to choose appropriate, responsible behavior.

This *Assertive Discipline Middle School Workbook* is your guide to implementing the revised Assertive Discipline program. The easy-to-follow format is concise and comfortable. Brief overviews of the program's key points are followed by the reproducible forms, positive notes, awards, raffle tickets, bookmarks, coupons, tracking sheets, communication and documentation pages, and visual aids that will allow you to successfully integrate the program into your teaching routine.

For a comprehensive understanding of the revised Assertive Discipline program, please read *Assertive Discipline—Positive Behavior Management for Today's Classroom.*

Positive Classroom Behavior Management and the Middle-School Classroom

Being a middle-school teacher is a challenging job—especially in today's world. You may find, like many teachers today, that it is increasingly difficult to establish a classroom environment free from disruptive behavior.

But in spite of the difficulties you face, you *can* create and maintain the kind of classroom in which you can effectively teach and your students can learn and grow academically and socially.

How can you achieve this? By becoming an assertive teacher—an empowered teacher—a teacher of influence. Whatever the age of your students, they will behave more responsibly and have more success in school if you follow these guidelines:

• Establish rules and specific directions that clearly define the limits of acceptable and unacceptable student behavior, that are fair and consistent.

• Teach your students to consistently follow these rules and directions, and to choose to behave responsibly, at all times when they are in your classroom.

• Provide students with consistent positive encouragement and recognition when they do behave. All children are eager for your positive words of encouragement and praise.

• Adopt a positive, assertive manner when responding to students. Students trust and respect the calm, consistent and caring presence of an assertive teacher. They know that the teacher has set limits and that he or she will follow through appropriately whenever a student chooses not to behave. There is no confusion, no second guessing, no hostility or anger.

• Remember to ask parents and administrators for their assistance when their support is needed. You can't do it alone. Education is a cooperative effort between teacher, student, parents and administration. Rely on each other for the positive assistance you can give.

Help your students make the most of their middle-school years. Create an atmosphere in which student self-esteem can flourish and you can feel accomplished at the end of every teaching day. Become a positive, proactive, assertive teacher—today!

S E C T I O N O N E

Your Classroom Discipline Plan

In this section of the *Assertive Discipline Middle School Workbook* we will first look at the classroom discipline plan— what it is and what it can do for you and your students. Then you will develop a discipline plan for your own classroom with rules, positives and consequences that best fit your needs, and the needs of your students.

Also included in this section is a wide variety of reproducibles that will help you successfully develop and implement your classroom discipline plan.

What Is a Classroom Discipline Plan?

A classroom discipline plan is a system that allows you to spell out the behaviors you expect from students and what they can expect from you in return. The plan provides a framework around which all of your classroom behavior management efforts can be organized.

The goal of a classroom discipline plan is to have a fair and consistent way to establish a safe, orderly, positive classroom environment in which you can teach and students can learn.

A classroom discipline plan consists of three parts:

- RULES that students must follow at all times.

- POSITIVE RECOGNITION that students will receive for following the rules.

- CONSEQUENCES that result when students choose not to follow the rules.

Here's a sample classroom discipline plan for a middle-school classroom:

CLASSROOM RULES
Follow directions.
Keep hands, feet and objects to yourself.
No swearing, teasing or name calling.
No yelling or screaming.

POSITIVE RECOGNITION
Praise
Positive notes sent home to parents
Positive notes to students
Coupons for student store
Select own seat for the day
No-homework pass

CONSEQUENCES

First time a student breaks a rule:	Warning
Second time:	Stay in class 1 minute after the bell
Third time:	Stay in class 2 minutes after the bell
Fourth time:	Teacher calls parents
Fifth time:	Send to principal
Severe Clause:	Send to principal

Benefits of a Classroom Discipline Plan

The middle-school years are a time when students are constantly testing limits. It is important, therefore, to have a classroom management structure in place that clearly indicates limits and boundaries.

Here are four reasons why a classroom discipline plan will help you create a positive learning environment in your classroom that benefits both you and your students.

1 A discipline plan makes managing student behavior easier.

Planning is the key to successful classroom management. When you have a plan for how you will respond to student behavior you won't have to make on-the-spot decisions about what to do when a student misbehaves—or how to properly recognize a student who does behave appropriately. You'll know what to do, your students will know what to expect, and the guesswork (and stress) will be eliminated from your daily disciplinary efforts.

2 A discipline plan protects students' rights.

All students have the right to the same due process in the classroom. A discipline plan will help ensure that you deal with each student in a fair and consistent manner.

3 A discipline plan helps ensure parental support.

When you communicate your discipline plan to parents (see pages 74-76), you are letting them know that you care about teaching their children to behave responsibly. This is a powerful message of support and professionalism to give to parents.

4 A discipline plan helps ensure administrator support.

A discipline plan demonstrates to your administrator that you have a well-thought-out course of action for managing student behavior in your classroom. When your administrator understands the commitment you've made to effective classroom management, you will be better able to get support when you need it.

It's Your Turn

Now we'll take you through the steps for creating a classroom discipline plan tailor made for you and your students.

First, you will plan the general rules for your classroom.

Second, you will choose the positive recognition you will use to motivate students to follow those rules.

Finally, you will learn how to most effectively select and use consequences when students choose not to follow the rules.

For team teachers or interdisciplinary teams:

To best meet the needs of your students—and to minimize confusion over varying expectations from teacher to teacher—consider developing a classroom discipline plan that will be consistent from classroom to classroom. After formulating the plan, the team meets once or twice during the quarter or semester to evaluate the effectiveness of the plan and make any changes necessary.

Creating Your Classroom Discipline Plan
Rules

Whether sixth-graders or eighth-graders, your students all share something in common when they arrive in your classroom—each brings a variety of behavioral expectations from home and a variety of behavioral expectations from previous teachers and schools.

These expectations, however, may not be *your* behavioral expectations.

Your students can't be expected to know how *you* want them to behave in your classroom unless you make those expectations clear to them.

General classroom rules, therefore, are the first part of your classroom discipline plan.

What are general classroom rules?

General classroom rules are those rules that are in place *all period long*—throughout all activities. These rules remain in effect whenever students are in your room, whether they are your homeroom students or students who come into your room throughout the day for instruction. General classroom rules are important because they let all of your students know what basic behavioral expectations you have at all times.

These guidelines will help you choose appropriate rules:

• Choose rules that are observable.
Address behaviors that you can clearly see. Vaguely stated expectations may mean one thing to one student, and an entirely different thing to another. As a result, they often cause problems by opening the door to arguments.

For example:

Observable Rules
Keep hands and feet to yourself.

Be in your seat when the bell rings.

No yelling or screaming.

Vague Expectations
Be kind to other students.

No fooling around when class starts.

No unnecessary talking.

• Choose rules that apply throughout the entire day or period.
General classroom rules are rules that apply all day, or all period, no matter what activity is taking place. These are rules that students are expected to follow at all times.

Now, before you choose your own rules, take a look at some rules that are *not* appropriate general classroom rules. Though often seen in classrooms, we have found that these rules are not appropriate general classroom rules because they are not applicable throughout the entire day.

Notice that while each rule *sounds* sensible, it cannot be a realistic ongoing expectation.

Rules to Avoid:

- Raise your hand and wait to be called upon before you speak.

There are going to be times when students are *expected* to speak out (for example, in cooperative learning groups). Therefore, this is not an appropriate general classroom rule.

- Stay in your seat unless you have permission to get up.

There may be many times during the day when it's OK for a student to get up without asking permission. Again, this rule may not be enforceable throughout the day.

- Use a 12-inch voice in the classroom.

Of course there will be times when students need to speak up! Do not make voice-level requirements part of your general classroom rules.

- Complete all homework assignments.

This rule does not relate to classroom behavior. Also, there may be times when completing homework is out of a student's control.

When you establish general classroom rules that do not clearly reflect your *consistent* expectations, you run the risk of confusing students, and you will not be able to enforce these rules with consistency.

Here are some general classroom rules that are appropriate for grades 6-8.

Notice that each of these rules is applicable throughout the entire day or class period—with any group of students.

Notice that each one is observable.

- Follow directions.
- Keep hands, feet and objects to yourself.
- Do not leave the room without permission.
- No swearing or teasing.
- No yelling or screaming.
- Bring all appropriate materials to class.

Involve students in choosing rules for the classroom.

Many teachers find it helpful to involve students in choosing some of the rules for the classroom. During a class discussion, ask students these questions: "How do other students stop you from learning? What rules would make it easier for you to learn?"

As the discussion progresses, guide students so that their suggested rules are both appropriate and realistic. Consider student input, but be sure that the final rules you choose follow the guidelines given and meet your own needs as a teacher.

By including students in the process of creating your rules, you will give them ownership in the classroom discipline plan. They will see the rules as their rules and will be more motivated to support and remind each other about following the rules.

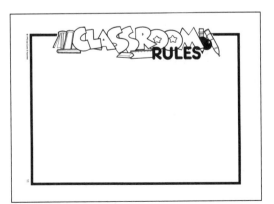

It's Your Turn

Use the Classroom Rules Worksheet on the next page to plan the general classroom rules you will use in your own classroom. When you're finished, write your rules on the Classroom Rules poster on page 11.

CLASSROOM RULES WORKSHEET

Use this worksheet to plan your own general classroom rules. We've started the list for you with the rule, "Follow directions." This is an important rule because students must be expected to follow any direction you might give during the day. When choosing the rest of your rules, remember: 1) Rules must be observable, and 2) Rules must apply throughout the entire day.

Classroom Rule: Follow directions.

This is an appropriate general classroom rule because:

_____

_____

_____

_____

Classroom Rule: _____

This is an appropriate general classroom rule because:

_____

_____

_____

_____

Classroom Rule: _____

This is an appropriate general classroom rule because:

_____

_____

_____

_____

Classroom Rule: _____

This is an appropriate general classroom rule because:

_____

_____

_____

_____

CLASSROOM RULES

Creating Your Classroom Discipline Plan
Positive Recognition

Your general classroom rules are the first part of your classroom discipline plan. The second part of your discipline plan, positive recognition, will help you motivate your students to follow these rules.

Positive recognition is the sincere and meaningful attention you give a student for behaving according to your expectations—for choosing the responsible behavior that will lead to greater success in school and increased self-esteem. Positive recognition is your opportunity to reach out to your students with the enthusiastic, caring attitude that middle-school students need. When consistently used, positive recognition will:

- Encourage your students to behave appropriately.

- Increase your students' self-esteem.

- Dramatically reduce problem behaviors.

- Create a positive classroom climate for you and your students.

- Help you teach appropriate behavior and establish positive relationships with your students.

> *Refer to pages 57-62 of the revised Assertive Discipline text for an in-depth look at these benefits of positive recognition.*

With these benefits in mind, let's take a look now at five ways you can provide positive recognition to individual students:

1 Praise

2 Positive notes and phone calls home

3 Special privileges

4 Certificates and awards

5 Tangible rewards

Praise

Do you know that the most meaningful *and* effective means of positive recognition you can give to students are your own words of praise?

When you take the time to say something positive about a student's achievement, you are making a statement that will have a long-lasting impact. You are saying, "I care about you. I notice the good work you are doing and I'm proud of you." That's an ego-boosting message that middle-school students need to hear as often as possible.

Praise, then, should be your #1 choice in positive recognition.

To ensure that the praise you give your students is as effective as possible, keep these guidelines in mind:

• Effective praise is personal.

After spending years in the nurturing environment of the self-contained elementary classroom, the middle school can seem like a pretty impersonal place. Students are changing classrooms and teachers all day long. Let students know that they are more than just one of hundreds of bodies. Maximize the impact of praise by including the student's name in your comments.

"Jena, you've done a wonderful job organizing your presentation."

"Ramon, thank you for working so well with Bradley on your science project."

• Effective praise must be genuine.

Young people recognize sincere words when they hear them. Make sure your words of praise genuinely reflect your own feelings of pride in a student's accomplishments. If your words ring false they won't mean a thing.

• Effective praise is descriptive and specific.

Praise will be most effective when it refers to something specific the student has accomplished. A specific comment such as, "I've noticed how well prepared for class you've been all this week, Nathan, and your efforts are paying off in better grades!" sounds much more meaningful than, "Great job, Nathan."

Note: As a middle-school teacher, you know that your students vary widely in maturity, temperament and personality. It is up to you, therefore, to exercise professional judgement when praising a student. Some students will appreciate and enjoy a verbal and public "round of applause" from time to time. Other students will appreciate a more private word of praise from you. Your goal is to build a student's self-esteem. With that in mind, deliver your praise in a manner that will be best received by the individual student.

It's Your Turn

Start thinking now about all of the opportunities you have each day to verbally recognize your students' successes—all of the moments when an admiring word from you can make a big difference in a student's life. Jot notes in your plan book reminding yourself to look for students' good behavior, then say something about it! Some middle-school teachers set a goal to give a minimum of five compliments per class period. Make that your goal, too, and you will be sure to positively reach 25 students each day.

Timely Reminders

As an extra reminder to praise students, make a copy of the "The Time Is Right for Responsible Behavior Choices" poster on page 14. Hang this reminder on the classroom wall right next to the clock. Throughout the day as you glance at the clock, this poster will be a gentle reminder to keep looking for positive behavior to reinforce.

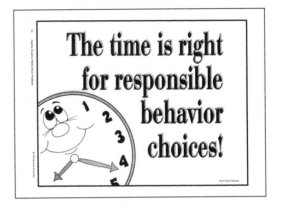

Looking for just the right moment to say "Good for you"?

There are hundreds of opportunities to praise students each day. Don't let these moments slip by. To help you further develop the praise habit, we've put together a list of "50 Opportunities to say 'You're Terrific'" (page 15). Keep this sheet in your desk or plan book and review it from time to time as a reminder of all the occasions throughout the school day in which you can verbally recognize a student's good behavior.

The time is right for responsible behavior choices!

50 OPPORTUNITIES TO SAY "YOU'RE TERRIFIC"

Praise students for:

1 entering the classroom quietly

2 arriving to class on time

3 cooperating while teacher takes attendance

4 returning permission slips and school forms on time

5 transitioning into an activity

6 following directions

7 saying "please" and "thank you"

8 listening attentively

9 helping a classmate

10 bringing necessary materials to class

11 handing in homework

12 being a polite audience at an assembly

13 beginning work right away

14 asking questions when unsure

15 good behavior during a test

16 participating in a class discussion

17 walking appropriately in the halls

18 working cooperatively with a partner

19 a performance in a play or presentation

20 cleaning up

21 good effort on an assignment

22 assisting a new student

23 sharing school experiences with parents

24 making up missed assignments

25 making a new friend

26 good effort on a long-term project

27 sharing

28 being sensitive to others' feelings

29 learning a new skill

30 appropriate use of school property

31 returning borrowed books and materials

32 showing enthusiasm

33 being responsible for a classroom job

34 offering help without being asked

35 not wasting paper and supplies

36 staying on task

37 telling the truth

38 accepting a new challenge

39 behaving when a guest is in the room

40 reading at home

41 participating in school functions

42 demonstrating a positive attitude

43 giving one's best effort

44 participating in a community improvement project

45 participating in a group activity

46 remaining calm during a problem situation

47 showing creativity

48 keeping busy when work is finished

49 taking turns

50 working cooperatively with an aide or volunteer

Positive Notes and Phone Calls

Good news in the mail or via the phone is always welcomed!

It makes sense, then, that positive notes and phone calls become an important part of your positive recognition planning.

The goal of a positive note or phone call is to share with parents "good news" about their child. This can be a gratifying change. After all, most parents never hear from school unless there is a problem.

Telling your students that you will send positive messages to parents about their responsible behavior is a great motivator. It is important for preadolescent students to know that their parents are proud of them and the work they are doing. Likewise, it's important for parents to know when their children are doing work they can be proud of.

It's also a great way to establish a positive relationship with parents. Throughout the year you will need parental support. It will be much easier to gain that support when you need it if you have already begun building a positive foundation. Most parents like nothing more than to hear something positive about their child.

Positive phone calls and notes don't take much time, but they pay big dividends.

Here's what a positive phone call to a parent might sound like.

> "Mrs. Robbins? This is Mr. Murray, Gary's teacher. I want you to know that Gary is making a great start at school this year. This first week we've spent a lot of time in our homeroom discussing classroom rules and expectations. I just wanted to let you know that Gary is following those rules *and* setting a great example.
>
> "Please tell Gary that I called and how pleased I am with his behavior in class."

Just that easy and just that quick. In a few brief moments this teacher has established a positive relationship with a parent and boosted the self-esteem of a student.

And here's what a positive note might say:

Dear Mr. and Mrs. Montoya,

I am so pleased to let you know what a wonderful job Carla is doing in my English class. She listens attentively and keeps a well-organized notebook. That's very important in keeping up with assignments, and in having the information she'll need to do homework. This kind of responsible behavior will help Carla do a good job in all of her classes. You should be very proud of the effort she's making.

Sincerely,

It's Your Turn

Once you recognize how easy it really is to make positive contact with parents, you'll be convinced that it's an effective use of your time. The suggestions that follow will help you develop this positive parent involvement habit.

First, set goals!

Set a goal to make a specific number of positive phone calls each week and to send a specific number of positive notes home each week. Just two contacts a day (10 a week) will guarantee that you reach 40 parents a month with good news. To make sure that all students receive this important attention, keep track of your positive contacts on the Positive Parent Communication Log on page 18. Create a sheet for each class, and check off whenever good news goes home.

Once you break the ice with parents, particularly with good news, you may find yourself picking up the phone more often—just to pass along some friendly, encouraging words.

Next, remember the good things that happen!

It's not always easy to remember the positive things students do during a busy day—especially when you have many students coming in and out of your classes. The answer? Use the Positive Memos on page 19 to jot down positive comments you want to remember and later share with parents in a phone call or in a note. Run off copies of the memos and keep them close by—different colors for different classes. During the day if something "memo"rable happens that you'd like to communicate, write it down! In some cases you may wish to keep this memo as part of a student's documentation file.

Finally, be sure to share the good news!

Use the positive notes on pages 20 and 21 any time you want parents and students to know how proud you are of a student's achievement. Run off copies of these reproducible notes, keep them handy, and use them frequently! (Keep track of notes sent home on the Positive Parent Communication Log.)

POSITIVE PARENT
COMMUNICATION LOG

Use this sheet to keep track of your positive communication efforts by circling
N for note, PC for phone call and O for other.

Student	Month of	Month of	Month of	Month of	Month of	Month of
	N PC O	N PC O	N PC O	N PC O	N PC O	N PC O
	N PC O	N PC O	N PC O	N PC O	N PC O	N PC O
	N PC O	N PC O	N PC O	N PC O	N PC O	N PC O
	N PC O	N PC O	N PC O	N PC O	N PC O	N PC O
	N PC O	N PC O	N PC O	N PC O	N PC O	N PC O
	N PC O	N PC O	N PC O	N PC O	N PC O	N PC O
	N PC O	N PC O	N PC O	N PC O	N PC O	N PC O
	N PC O	N PC O	N PC O	N PC O	N PC O	N PC O
	N PC O	N PC O	N PC O	N PC O	N PC O	N PC O
	N PC O	N PC O	N PC O	N PC O	N PC O	N PC O
	N PC O	N PC O	N PC O	N PC O	N PC O	N PC O
	N PC O	N PC O	N PC O	N PC O	N PC O	N PC O
	N PC O	N PC O	N PC O	N PC O	N PC O	N PC O
	N PC O	N PC O	N PC O	N PC O	N PC O	N PC O
	N PC O	N PC O	N PC O	N PC O	N PC O	N PC O
	N PC O	N PC O	N PC O	N PC O	N PC O	N PC O
	N PC O	N PC O	N PC O	N PC O	N PC O	N PC O
	N PC O	N PC O	N PC O	N PC O	N PC O	N PC O
	N PC O	N PC O	N PC O	N PC O	N PC O	N PC O
	N PC O	N PC O	N PC O	N PC O	N PC O	N PC O
	N PC O	N PC O	N PC O	N PC O	N PC O	N PC O

POSITIVE MEMO

Student's name_____ Parent's name_____

Phone number_____ Date_____ Period/Class_____

Positive news to share with parents:

_____

_____

_____

_____

_____

- -

POSITIVE MEMO

Student's name_____ Parent's name_____

Phone number_____ Date_____ Period/Class_____

Positive news to share with parents:

_____

_____

_____

_____

_____

- -

POSITIVE MEMO

Student's name_____ Parent's name_____

Phone number_____ Date_____ Period/Class_____

Positive news to share with parents:

_____

_____

_____

_____

_____

Great News to Share!

_____

_____

_____

_____

Signed   Date

GREAT! TERRIFIC! HOORAY! FABULOUS!

_____

_____

_____

_____

_____

_____

_____

_____

Signed

_____

Date

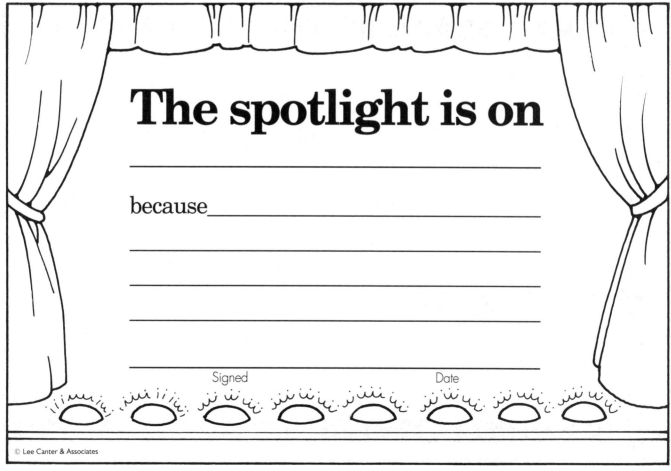

The spotlight is on

_____

because_____

_____

_____

_____

Signed   Date

Behavior Awards

Special awards for responsible behavior will help motivate middle-school students because they have a double impact!

1 Students will be proud to receive them from you, and

2 they'll be proud to take them home to show to parents!

Tell students that one way you'll recognize their responsible behavior throughout the year is by sending home special awards that let them *and* their parents know how responsibly they are behaving in school.

To keep yourself on track, plan to send home a specific number of awards each week.

It's Your Turn

• Good Behavior "Designer" Bookmarks

Fun and functional, each of these bookmarks carries a positive message of recognition PLUS a graphic design that students can color in and keep.

• Good Behavior Bookmark/Raffle Ticket Combos

There's a bonus attached to these bookmarks! Each motivating (and useful) bookmark also contains a raffle ticket. Each time a student is awarded a bookmark, he or she also earns the right to enter a raffle drawing. The student fills the ticket out and deposits it into a class collection box. Once a week (or every two weeks, etc.) the teacher draws a pre-determined number of tickets and awards privileges or prizes.

Or try this: At the beginning of the week, pass out a bookmark to each student. Explain that as the week goes by you will recognize good behavior by allowing students to enter their ticket portions in a class raffle.

• Notable Student Bookmarks

Recognize a student's "notable" behavior with these "Notes, etc." bookmarks. Space for name of class, name of textbook, lines for jotting notes or personal thoughts—plus a positive message!

• Behavior Certificates

Students and their parents will appreciate the humorous (but sincere) behavior certificates on pages 27-28. Just fill in the specific behavior you want to recognize and present the award to the deserving student, or send home to parents.

• Quick-Notes to Parents

These quick-notes are an easy way to send a positive message to parents. Keep a stack close by, and when you are grading papers and would like to share some positive news just fill one out and staple to the paper.

• Quick-Notes to Students

A teacher's written comments to a student can have a long-lasting and positive impact. Quick Notes are a simple way to pass along a few good words. Just fill out and staple to corrected papers.

• Certificate of Appreciation

This full-page certificate can be used to recognize good behavior, or any other occasion deserving of praise.

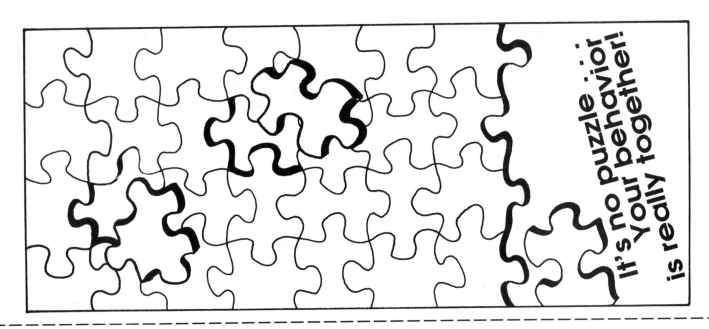

No puzzle . . .
It's no behavior!
Your together!
is really

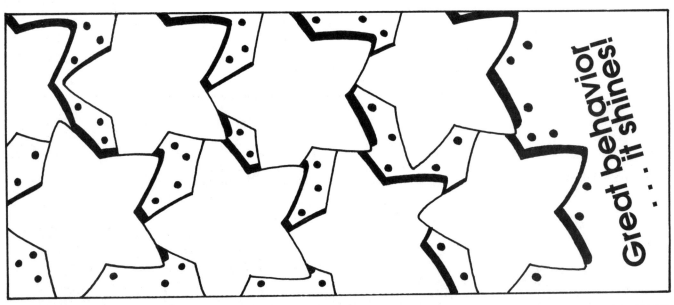

Great behavior!
Your behavior
. . . it shines!

Your behavior!
is in great shape!

Notes, etc.

...for being a "notable" student!

DOODLES

Notes, etc.

...for being a "notable" student!

DOODLES

Notes, etc.

...for being a "notable" student!

DOODLES

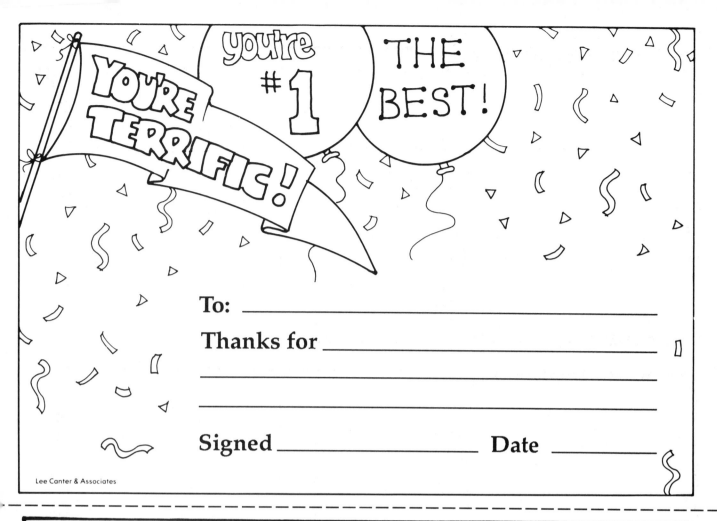

You're TERRIFIC!

you're #1

THE BEST!

To: _____

Thanks for _____

_____

_____

Signed _____ Date _____

Lee Canter & Associates

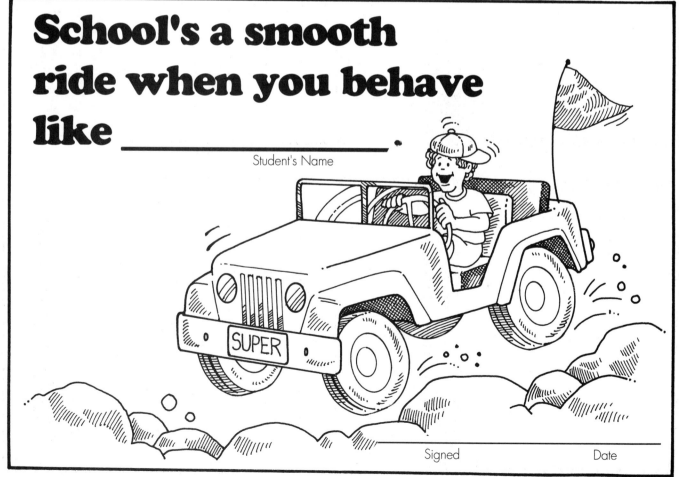

School's a smooth ride when you behave like _____.

Student's Name

Signed _____ Date _____

To: _____

I'd like to say a few
words about the way you
behave in class . . .

 GOOD JOB!

 TERRIFIC!

SUPER!

_____
Signed   Date

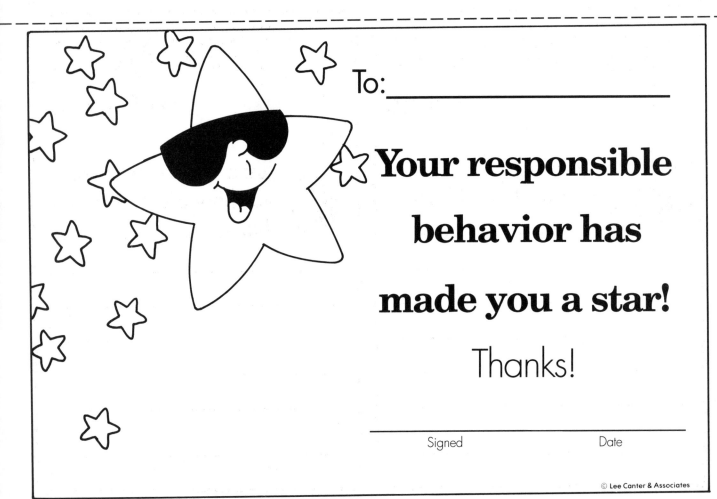

To: _____

Your responsible behavior has made you a star!

Thanks!

_____
Signed   Date

QUICK NOTE
to Parents

To: _____

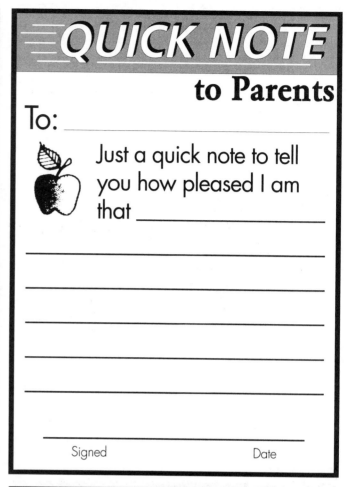 Just a quick note to tell you how pleased I am that _____

_____

_____

_____

_____

_____

_____

Signed _____   Date _____

QUICK NOTE
to Parents

To: _____

Just a quick note to tell you how pleased I am that _____

_____

_____

_____

_____

_____

_____

Signed _____   Date _____

QUICK NOTE
to Parents

To: _____

Just a quick note to tell you how pleased I am that _____

_____

_____

_____

_____

_____

_____

Signed _____   Date _____

QUICK NOTE
to Parents

To: _____

Just a quick note to tell you how pleased I am that _____

_____

_____

_____

_____

_____

_____

Signed _____   Date _____

QUICK NOTE
to Students

To: _____

Just a quick note to let
you know _____

_____

_____

_____

_____

_____

_____
Signed   Date

QUICK NOTE
to Students

To: _____

Just a quick note to let
you know _____

_____

_____

_____

_____

_____

_____
Signed   Date

QUICK NOTE
to Students

To: _____

Just a quick note to let
you know _____

_____

_____

_____

_____

_____

_____
Signed   Date

QUICK NOTE
to Students

To: _____

Just a quick note to let
you know _____

_____

_____

_____

_____

_____

_____
Signed   Date

Certificate of

Appreciation

presented to

For

Teacher's Signature

Date

Special Privileges

When you want to recognize a student's positive behavior, and motivate him or her to continue that behavior, allow the student to take part in an activity that he or she particularly enjoys.

Special privileges are great motivators because students like to receive them and they don't have to cost anything to give.

Here are some ideas to get you started. Add ideas of your own that will appeal to your students on the lines that follow.

- First excused from class
- Classroom monitor
- Correct papers
- Listen to music on cassette with headset
- 10 minutes free time
- Extra computer time
- Work on a favorite activity
- _____
- _____
- _____
- _____
- _____
- _____
- _____
- _____
- _____
- _____
- _____
- _____
- _____
- _____

It's Your Turn

Just ask 'em!

Not sure what special privileges will motivate your students? Your students will be more than happy to give their opinions on this matter! Give students the "Wish List" menu on the next page. We have started the list with some privileges that middle-school students enjoy. Add your own ideas to the list, then ask students to write in suggestions of their own.

Tell students that you want their feedback because throughout the year you will be awarding special privileges to students who behave responsibly at school. Tie this activity into a brief class discussion and you're sure to gather lots of motivating suggestions!

You Earned It!

When a student earns a special privilege for good behavior, fill out a "You Earned It!" coupon.

These open-ended coupons are great for sharing the good news with students *and* they're easy to complete. Sprinkle in some praise with your presentation and make the recognition even more meaningful.

> "Ellen, you worked cooperatively with your science group today without any reminders or warnings. Because of that, your group accomplished a lot! Here's a reward coupon for you. You earned it!"

Get parents involved, too!

Send home a small supply of "You Earned It" coupons to parents. In a brief note, encourage them to use the coupons at home to congratulate their children for good schoolwork, good behavior at school or at home, or as a recognition for being a caring, responsible member of the family. (Back-to-School Night is a good time to explain these coupons to parents and distribute copies to parents.

WISH LIST OF SPECIAL PRIVILEGES

Name_____Class/Period_____

Check off three things that you like to do best at school. If you have any
suggestions of your own, add them to the list.

- ❏ First excused after class
- ❏ Classroom monitor
- ❏ 10 minutes free time
- ❏ Extra computer time
- ❏ Correct papers.

❏ _____
❏ _____
❏ _____
❏ _____
❏ _____

- -

WISH LIST OF SPECIAL PRIVILEGES

Name_____Class/Period_____

Check off three things that you like to do best at school. If you have any
suggestions of your own, add them to the list.

- ❏ First excused after class
- ❏ Classroom monitor
- ❏ 10 minutes free time
- ❏ Extra computer time
- ❏ Correct papers.

❏ _____
❏ _____
❏ _____
❏ _____
❏ _____

- -

WISH LIST OF SPECIAL PRIVILEGES

Name_____Class/Period_____

Check off three things that you like to do best at school. If you have any
suggestions of your own, add them to the list.

- ❏ First excused after class
- ❏ Classroom monitor
- ❏ 10 minutes free time
- ❏ Extra computer time
- ❏ Correct papers.

❏ _____
❏ _____
❏ _____
❏ _____
❏ _____

TO:_____

"You Earned It"

_____

FOR:_____

_____

Date

TO:_____

"You Earned It"

_____

FOR:_____

_____

Date

TO:_____

"You Earned It"

_____

FOR:_____

_____

Date

TO:_____

"You Earned It"

_____

FOR:_____

_____

Date

TO:_____

"You Earned It"

_____

FOR:_____

_____

Date

TO:_____

"You Earned It"

_____

FOR:_____

_____

Date

TO:_____

"You Earned It"

_____

FOR:_____

_____

Date

TO:_____

"You Earned It"

_____

FOR:_____

_____

Date

Tangible Rewards

Most students are motivated by praise, positive notes and special privileges. You may, however, have one or two students who simply do not respond to these positive reinforcers. There are times when tangible rewards such as a small prize or trinket are the only positives that will work—the only way you can motivate a student (of any age). When needed, use tangible rewards, but use them with care.

Follow these guidelines:

• Be sure to give a tangible reward immediately after you have observed the desired behavior. You want the student to associate this behavior with the reward.

• Whenever you give a student a tangible reward, always pair it with your own praise such as,

"Joel, here's a neon pencil for sitting so quietly during the lesson. I appreciate how responsibly you behaved."

"Janice, here's a pencil topper for taking your seat so quickly and quietly when you came into the classroom. By coming in so nicely we all are able to get to work right away."

Tangible rewards are particularly effective on those hard-to-motivate days when students tend to become overly excited (for example, on Fridays, days before holidays, and days when special school events are scheduled).

It's Your Turn

We've looked at five ways you can positively reinforce students for following the rules of the classroom:

1 Praise

2 Positive notes and phone calls home

3 Special privileges

4 Behavior awards

5 Tangible awards

Now it's time to plan the positives you will use with individual students in your own classroom. As you plan, be sure to include positives that you are comfortable giving, that students will enjoy receiving and, most importantly, ones that you will be able to give frequently and consistently.

When you're finished planning, write your positives on the poster on page 37. (Tuck the finished poster away with your supplies. You'll be using it when you introduce your classroom discipline plan to your students.)

Classwide Positive Recognition

Just as you recognize individual students for their appropriate behavior, you can also recognize your entire class for meeting expectations. A classwide positive recognition system makes it easy.

What is a classwide positive recognition system?

A classwide positive recognition system is a program in which all of your students, not just one student, work together toward a positive reward that will be given to the entire class.

The goal of a classwide recognition system is to motivate students to learn a new behavior or to work on improving a problem behavior. It shows students how important it is to work together in a cooperative manner to achieve a common goal.

Keep these points in mind when considering a classwide recognition system:

- A powerful reason why a classwide recognition system works well with middle-school students is because it makes use of peer pressure. It's not uncommon for students to cooperatively remind each other, "Listen to the teacher. If we get four more points, we get free time on Friday."

- A classwide recognition system is particularly effective when working on a specific classwide problem behavior such as students noisily entering the classroom.

- To be effective, a classwide recognition system should be implemented as needed throughout the year. It is not meant to be in effect at all times. A classwide system is designed to be used as a prescription for correcting a specific problem.

Here's how to set up a classwide recognition program:

1. Pick a system that you are comfortable with and that is appropriate to the age of your students. On pages 39-43 you will find directions and artwork for creating a positive behavior bulletin board especially designed for middle-school students.

2. Choose a classwide reward that you are comfortable giving, but make sure that whatever reward the class earns, it is something they will want to work toward.

Here are some ideas for classwide rewards:

- Special movie or video
- Free time in class
- Invite a special visitor to class
- Popcorn party
- 1/2 hour study hall to get homework done
- Listen to music in class
- Play a game in class

3. Make sure students are able to earn the reward in a timely manner. Set a goal for how quickly you want the class to earn a reward. Then monitor the frequency with which you are awarding points to ensure that you and the students are on track. Middle-school students typically should be able to earn the classwide reward in one to two weeks.

4. Once the class has earned points toward a classwide reward, do not take away points for misbehavior. Also, keep in mind that all students, regardless of negative consequences they may have earned individually, must participate in the classwide reward. If you impose a consequence and take away the classwide reward, you are providing two consequences for one misbehavior.

It's Your Turn

The following pages contain artwork and instructions for creating a positive bulletin board for your classroom.

WE'RE LETTERING IN SUPER BEHAVIOR!

Period 1	S	U	P	E	R	*Congratulations*
Period 3	S	U				
Period 5	S	U	P			

Generating "Class Spirit"

Encourage your middle-school students to "get in the spirit" and behave appropriately with this classwide positive recognition system. The entire class is rewarded with a sports mascot "letter" for each day everyone behaves appropriately throughout the entire period. When the class has earned all five sports letters, spelling S-U-P-E-R, they are rewarded with a special privilege or activity.

The program is simple to implement:

- Create the headline "We're Lettering in Super Behavior" and place on a bulletin board.

- Create a grid (on poster board or butcher paper) on which you can write each participating class's name and pin each of the letters (pages 40-42) and the Congratulations Reward Poster (page 43).

- Arrange on bulletin board according to sample above.

- Write the names of each participating class (Period 1, 3, etc.) on the grid.

- Enthusiastically introduce the bulletin board to each class. Explain that the class will be rewarded with a sports mascot "letter" each day that they follow directions appropriately. When all the letters in the word "SUPER" have been awarded to the class, they will earn a special privilege or activity—free class time, exchanging seats for the period, background music during independent study, etc.

- Write in the reward on the special mascot poster on page 43 and place on the grid when the class has earned all five letters.

Note: This activity may not be appropriate for all your classes, but you can do the program

41

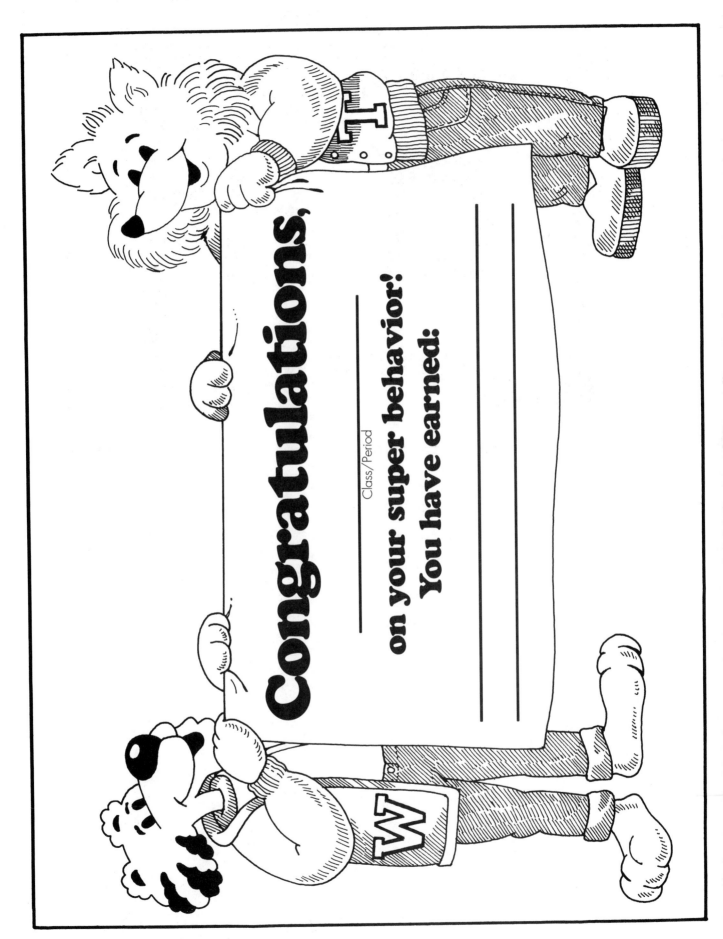

Congratulations,

Class/Period

on your super behavior!
You have earned:

Creating Your Classroom Discipline Plan
Consequences

In spite of the care you take in choosing your rules, and in spite of your consistent attention to positive recognition, there will be times when some students will choose not to follow the rules of your classroom. When this disruptive behavior occurs, you must be prepared to deal with it calmly and quickly.

Consequences are the third part of your classroom discipline plan.

Why are consequences important?

By carefully planning consequences, by knowing in advance what you will do when students misbehave, you won't be caught off guard or left wondering how to respond to a student's misbehavior. And that means that students will be treated fairly and *you* will feel less stress.

Follow these guidelines when choosing consequences for your classroom:

• Consequences are a choice.
Students in grades 6 through 8 are learning that they are responsible for their own actions and their own behavior. It's important, therefore, that consequences be presented to students as a choice. When a teacher gives students a choice, he or she places responsibility where it belongs, on the student.

For example:

Teacher: Michael, our classroom rule is no yelling. If you yell a second time, you will choose to stay one minute after class. It's your choice, Michael.

Michael: Okay. (*Within two minutes, Michael yells to a friend across the room.*)

Teacher: Michael, you are yelling in class again. You have chosen to stay one minute after class.

Remember—**choice** is the key word. When you give students a choice, they learn that they can be in control of what happens to them. Keep in mind that consequences are *not* punishment. Consequences are actions students know will occur should they choose to break the rules of the classroom. Consequences must be seen as natural outcomes of inappropriate behavior.

• Consequences do not have to be severe to be effective.
Teachers often think that the more severe a consequence, the more impact it will have on a student. This is not true. The key to effective consequences is that they are used *consistently*. It is the inevitability of the consequence, not the severity, that makes it effective. Minimal consequences, such as remaining in the classroom one minute after the dismissal bell or spending five minutes working away from the group can be as effective as after-school detention when they are given consistently.

And keep this in mind: The easier it is for you to give consequences, the more likely it will be that you will use them.

• Consequences must be something that students do not like, but they must never be physically or psychologically harmful.

How to Use Consequences:
Establishing a Discipline Hierarchy

The best way to use consequences with your students is to organize them into a discipline hierarchy as part of your classroom discipline plan.

A discipline hierarchy lists consequences in the order in which they will be imposed for disruptive behavior within a day or within a class period.

- The hierarchy is progressive, starting with a warning.

- The consequences then become gradually more substantial for the second, third, fourth, and fifth time that a student chooses to disrupt.

Self-contained or Departmentalized Classrooms

Whether your class structure is self-contained, departmentalized or in grade-level teams, your discipline hierarchy will be progressive for the length of time your students are in your room.

If your students are with you all day, consequences need to be progressive throughout the entire day. If students are only in your room for one period, your consequences must progress for that period only.

Whatever the structure, when students return to class the next day they enter your room with a clean slate—consequences do not accumulate for more than one day.

Here's how the discipline hierarchy works:

First Time a Student Disrupts

Always give a warning the first time a student disrupts or breaks a classroom rule.

This is an important first consequence because a warning gives the student an opportunity to choose more appropriate behavior before a more substantial consequence is given.

Second or Third Time a Student Disrupts

The second or third time a student disrupts in the same day, you need to provide a consequence.

These consequences should be easy to implement and not time consuming. Typical consequences for second or third infractions include staying one minute after class, staying two minutes after class, time out and writing in a behavior journal. (See page 30 for further discussion about these consequences.)

Fourth Time a Student Disrupts

Four disruptions during one day or period are completely unacceptable. You need to contact parents if a student disrupts a fourth time in a day (or class period).

For some students, involving parents will be the only way you will motivate them to behave appropriately. Students need to know that you will be consistent in the enforcement of this consequence. Any time a student reaches the fourth level of the discipline hierarchy parents must be contacted.

Fifth Time a Student Disrupts

Sending a student to the principal or vice principal should be the last consequence on your discipline hierarchy.

In preparation for implementing this consequence, you must have already met with your administrator and discussed the actions he or she will take when students are sent to the office (see pages 54-55).

Severe Clause

Sometimes you have to act quickly and decisively to stop a student's disruptive behavior. In cases of severe misbehavior, such as fighting, vandalism, defying a teacher or in some way stopping the entire class from functioning, a student would not receive a warning. He or she loses the right to proceed through the hierarchy of consequences. Severe misbehavior calls for an immediate consequence that will remove the student from the classroom.

Here are two sample discipline hierarchies for middle-school classrooms:

First time a student breaks a rule:	Warning
Second time:	10 minutes working away from the group
Third time:	15 minutes working away from the group plus write in behavior journal
Fourth time:	Call parents
Fifth time:	Send to principal
Severe Clause:	Send to principal

First time a student breaks a rule:	Warning
Second time:	Stay after class one minute
Third time:	Stay after class two minutes
Fourth time:	Call parents
Fifth time:	Send to principal
Severe Clause:	Send to principal

Keeping Track of Consequences

For your discipline hierarchy to be simple to use and easy to integrate into your teaching routine, you will need a system to keep track of student misbehavior and consequences accrued. You'll need to know at a glance the names of students who have received consequences, and where they are on the hierarchy.

Keeping track doesn't have to be time consuming and, most important, it doesn't have to interrupt your teaching.

One method of keeping track of consequences is the Behavior Tracking Sheet (page 47). Another is the "8 in 1" sheet (page 49).

Using a Behavior Tracking Sheet

Here's how a Behavior Tracking Sheet works:

Make copies of the Behavior Tracking Sheet on page 48. (Designate a different sheet for each class.) Attach to a clipboard and keep close by throughout the day.

Follow these guidelines:

First time a student breaks a rule.

Write down his or her name on the sheet and say, for example, "Chris, the rule is 'Keep your hands to yourself.' This is a warning."

- Circle the "Warning" designation on the tracking sheet.

Second time a student breaks a rule.

Speak quietly and calmly to the student saying, for example, "Chris, this is the second time you have broken a rule in this classroom today. You have chosen to stay in class one minute after the bell rings."

- Circle the "2" on the tracking sheet, indicating that this is the second infraction of the day. As noted above, the student has been informed that he is to stay in the classroom for one minute after the bell rings.

Third, fourth or fifth time a student breaks a rule.

If a student breaks a rule a third, fourth or fifth time during the day, you must continue speaking quietly and calmly to the student, and continue recording the infractions on the tracking sheet. Make sure that the consequences are given according to your hierarchy. If your third consequence is detention, be sure you follow through. If your fourth consequence is "call parents," be sure that you make that phone call. The success of your discipline plan depends upon your consistency.

Note: Space is allotted on the tracking sheet for brief comments. For some students you may wish to jot down the rule broken. Then, if you notice a pattern of behavior developing, you will have documentation to help you solve that problem.

BEHAVIOR TRACKING SHEET

WEEK OF _____

Name	MONDAY	TUESDAY	WEDNESDAY	THURSDAY	FRIDAY
Chris R.	(Warning) (2) 3 4 5	Warning 2 3 4 5	Warning 2 3 4 5	Warning 2 3 4 5	Warning 2 3 4 5
	Warning 2 3 4 5	Warning 2 3 4 5	Warning 2 3 4 5	Warning 2 3 4 5	Warning 2 3 4 5
	Warning 2 3 4 5	Warning 2 3 4 5	Warning 2 3 4 5	Warning 2 3 4 5	Warning 2 3 4 5
	Warning 2 3 4 5	Warning 2 3 4 5	Warning 2 3 4 5	Warning 2 3 4 5	Warning 2 3 4 5
	Warning 2 3 4 5	Warning 2 3 4 5	Warning 2 3 4 5	Warning 2 3 4 5	Warning 2 3 4 5
	Warning 2 3 4 5	Warning 2 3 4 5	Warning 2 3 4 5	Warning 2 3 4 5	Warning 2 3 4 5
	Warning 2 3 4 5	Warning 2 3 4 5	Warning 2 3 4 5	Warning 2 3 4 5	Warning 2 3 4 5
	Warning 2 3 4 5	Warning 2 3 4 5	Warning 2 3 4 5	Warning 2 3 4 5	Warning 2 3 4 5
	Warning 2 3 4 5	Warning 2 3 4 5	Warning 2 3 4 5	Warning 2 3 4 5	Warning 2 3 4 5
	Warning 2 3 4 5	Warning 2 3 4 5	Warning 2 3 4 5	Warning 2 3 4 5	Warning 2 3 4 5
	Warning 2 3 4 5	Warning 2 3 4 5	Warning 2 3 4 5	Warning 2 3 4 5	Warning 2 3 4 5
	Warning 2 3 4 5	Warning 2 3 4 5	Warning 2 3 4 5	Warning 2 3 4 5	Warning 2 3 4 5
	Warning 2 3 4 5	Warning 2 3 4 5	Warning 2 3 4 5	Warning 2 3 4 5	Warning 2 3 4 5
	Warning 2 3 4 5	Warning 2 3 4 5	Warning 2 3 4 5	Warning 2 3 4 5	Warning 2 3 4 5
	Warning 2 3 4 5	Warning 2 3 4 5	Warning 2 3 4 5	Warning 2 3 4 5	Warning 2 3 4 5
	Warning 2 3 4 5	Warning 2 3 4 5	Warning 2 3 4 5	Warning 2 3 4 5	Warning 2 3 4 5

To the teacher: When a student receives a warning, write the student's name on this tracking sheet. If a student breaks additional rules during that school day, circle each consequence on the appropriate box. For example, if a student receives a warning and chooses not to follow the rules again during the day, you would record (Warning) (2) (3) 4 5.

48

Assertive Discipline Middle School Workbook

© 1992 Lee Canter & Associates

BEHAVIOR TRACKING SHEET

WEEK OF _____

Name	MONDAY	TUESDAY	WEDNESDAY	THURSDAY	FRIDAY
	Warning 2 3 4 5	Warning 2 3 4 5	Warning 2 3 4 5	Warning 2 3 4 5	Warning 2 3 4 5
	Warning 2 3 4 5	Warning 2 3 4 5	Warning 2 3 4 5	Warning 2 3 4 5	Warning 2 3 4 5
	Warning 2 3 4 5	Warning 2 3 4 5	Warning 2 3 4 5	Warning 2 3 4 5	Warning 2 3 4 5
	Warning 2 3 4 5	Warning 2 3 4 5	Warning 2 3 4 5	Warning 2 3 4 5	Warning 2 3 4 5
	Warning 2 3 4 5	Warning 2 3 4 5	Warning 2 3 4 5	Warning 2 3 4 5	Warning 2 3 4 5
	Warning 2 3 4 5	Warning 2 3 4 5	Warning 2 3 4 5	Warning 2 3 4 5	Warning 2 3 4 5
	Warning 2 3 4 5	Warning 2 3 4 5	Warning 2 3 4 5	Warning 2 3 4 5	Warning 2 3 4 5
	Warning 2 3 4 5	Warning 2 3 4 5	Warning 2 3 4 5	Warning 2 3 4 5	Warning 2 3 4 5
	Warning 2 3 4 5	Warning 2 3 4 5	Warning 2 3 4 5	Warning 2 3 4 5	Warning 2 3 4 5
	Warning 2 3 4 5	Warning 2 3 4 5	Warning 2 3 4 5	Warning 2 3 4 5	Warning 2 3 4 5
	Warning 2 3 4 5	Warning 2 3 4 5	Warning 2 3 4 5	Warning 2 3 4 5	Warning 2 3 4 5
	Warning 2 3 4 5	Warning 2 3 4 5	Warning 2 3 4 5	Warning 2 3 4 5	Warning 2 3 4 5
	Warning 2 3 4 5	Warning 2 3 4 5	Warning 2 3 4 5	Warning 2 3 4 5	Warning 2 3 4 5
	Warning 2 3 4 5	Warning 2 3 4 5	Warning 2 3 4 5	Warning 2 3 4 5	Warning 2 3 4 5
	Warning 2 3 4 5	Warning 2 3 4 5	Warning 2 3 4 5	Warning 2 3 4 5	Warning 2 3 4 5
	Warning 2 3 4 5	Warning 2 3 4 5	Warning 2 3 4 5	Warning 2 3 4 5	Warning 2 3 4 5
	Warning 2 3 4 5	Warning 2 3 4 5	Warning 2 3 4 5	Warning 2 3 4 5	Warning 2 3 4 5
	Warning 2 3 4 5	Warning 2 3 4 5	Warning 2 3 4 5	Warning 2 3 4 5	Warning 2 3 4 5

To the teacher: When a student receives a warning, write the student's name on this tracking sheet. If a student breaks additional rules during that school day, circle each consequence on the appropriate box. For example, if a student receives a warning and chooses not to follow the rules again during the day, you would record Warning ②③ 4 5.

Using an "8 in 1" Tracking Sheet

Here's an easy tracking method that fits right in your pocket!

- Fold a sheet of lined paper into quarters as shown.

- Write the date on the top of the sheet.

- In each of the eight sections (front and back) designate a period:

  Period 1, Period 2, Period 3, etc.

- During the period if a student breaks a rule or disrupts, simply write his or her name, following it with the number of the classroom rule broken. (If you use this method, your classroom rules must be numbered: For example, Rule #1—Follow directions.)

- At the end of each day file the sheet in a notebook, or transfer the information to student's permanent records.

In this sample, you can see that Sue W. has broken Rule #1. Later in the period she breaks Rule #3:

Suggested Consequences

Here are consequences that have proven effective with middle-school students:

One Minute Wait After Class

It sounds deceptively simple, but this is a consequence that students do not like and it works. You simply have the student wait one minute after the other students have been dismissed for recess, lunch, home or the next period. One minute may not seem like a lot of time to you, but it can be an eternity to a student who wants to be first in line at the cafeteria, sit with a friend on the bus, or walk to the next class with his or her group. Don't underestimate the power of this consequence!

A one-minute wait after class is an appropriate consequence for the second time a rule is broken in a day or period. A two-minute wait is appropriate the third time a rule is broken.

Time Out—Removing a Student from the Group

Removing a disruptive student from the group is not a new concept, but it is a very effective consequence for some middle-school students. Designate a chair or table as the "time-out area," or simply relocate the student to a place in the room where he or she will not be likely to repeat the disruptive behavior. A trip to the time-out area could last from five to fifteen minutes.

> Note: It's very important that students not be isolated from the rest of the class for long lengths of time. Keep your time within these limits. Important: While separated from the rest of the class, the student continues to do his or her classwork.

Written Assignment in Behavior Journal

You want more from consequences than a student feeling contrite. You want the student to learn from the experience. That's critical if your middle-school students are to learn to choose responsible behavior. You want students to think about their behavior, and how they can choose to behave differently in the future.

When a student breaks a classroom rule, have him or her write a "Behavior Journal" account of this misbehavior either after class, during recess or lunch break, or at home. This written account should include the following points:

1. The rule that was broken.

   "The rule I broke was no swearing."

2. Why the student chose to break the rule or not follow the direction.

   "I swore at Lisa because she was teasing me. She said that my haircut made me look like a potato."

3. What alternative action the student could have taken that would have been more appropriate.

   "Instead of swearing at Lisa I could have ignored her. I could have walked away and talked to my friends."

The student signs and dates the Behavior Journal sheet. The sheet should then be added to the student's documentation records. (It can also be sent home to parents as documentation of the student's misbehavior.)

The Behavior Journal sheet can also be used as the focus for a meeting with the student to discuss how teacher and student can work together to improve the problem behavior. Writing in a behavior journal helps students accept responsibility for their behavior. It also helps them think about choosing alternative behaviors in the future.

It's Your Turn

On page 51 you will find a reproducible Behavior Journal sheet. Make copies of this sheet and use it as part of your discipline hierarchy.

Write the consequences you choose on the poster on page 52.

BEHAVIOR JOURNAL

Student's Name _____ Class/Period_____ Date_____

This is the rule I broke: _____

_____

I chose to break this rule because: _____

_____

_____

_____

_____

_____

_____

_____

_____

This is what I could have done instead: _____

_____

_____

_____

_____

_____

Student Signature   Date

S E C T I O N T W O

Launching Your Classroom Discipline Plan

Your discipline plan is written. You've chosen the rules for your classroom, the positive recognition you will give when students follow the rules, and the consequences students will receive when they choose to break the rules.

Ready to put it all into action?

Not quite.

The success of your classroom discipline plan depends on more than your planning and involvement alone. It also depends on the informed involvement of others who will be affected by it: your students, your students' parents and your administrator.

In this section of the *Assertive Discipline Middle School Workbook* we will look at techniques for introducing your discipline plan. Also included is a selection of reproducibles to help you plan and carry out an effective introduction.

Talk to Your Administrator About Your Classroom Discipline Plan

Your administrator is an integral part of your behavior management program. No matter how well prepared you are, no matter how consistently and positively you use your discipline plan, you may still have some students that you will not be able to influence on your own. You are going to need the cooperation and assistance of your principal or vice principal. The best way to ensure that cooperation is to involve him or her from the very beginning.

Before you put your classroom discipline plan into effect, you should meet with your administrator to discuss his or her role in your discipline plan.

Involving your administrator is important for two reasons.

First, if you send a student to the office, according to your discipline hierarchy, your principal, vice principal or administrator will want to know what steps you have already taken to deal with the problem.

Second, so that you can follow up with a student, you will want to know exactly what action the principal or vice principal will take when a student is sent to him or her.

Make an appointment with your principal or vice principal before school begins. Follow these guidelines for presenting your plan:

Explain your rationale for using a classroom discipline plan.

Begin by explaining why you are using a classroom discipline plan. Let your administrator know that you are committed to having a classroom that is safe and orderly, a positive learning environment for your students, and a positive teaching environment for yourself. Explain that this is the reason you have established a classroom discipline plan with rules for behavior, positive recognition for students who choose to follow the rules and consequences for students who choose to break the rules.

Emphasize that you will attempt to handle behavior problems on your own before you ever ask for the principal's help.

Your principal needs to know that before you send a student to the office, you will have already taken steps to deal with the student's misbehavior on your own.

Ask the administrator for input.

Prepare a copy of your classroom discipline plan for your administrator. During your meeting, ask for input to make sure that he or she is comfortable with all aspects of the plan. If your administrator is not comfortable, ask for assistance in modifying the plan.

Discuss what the administrator will do when a student is sent from your class to the office.

You need to know exactly what will happen when you send a student to your administrator.

Many administrators follow a hierarchy of consequences, too. Here are some examples:

First time sent to office

Counsel with the student and suggest other ways the student could have handled the situation.

Second time sent to office

Hold a parent conference to discuss the problem. Ask parents to support the school's efforts by taking away privileges at home.

Third time sent to office

In-school suspension. The student does schoolwork outside of the regular classroom and in a closely supervised environment.

Severe

Counsel with the student and have a parent conference.

It is important that your administrator lets you know what type of disciplinary action will be taken so you can follow up appropriately with parents and student. This follow up can be accomplished by sending a note home or having a short meeting after school.

Discuss what will happen if the administrator is out of the building.

There may be times when you need to remove a disruptive student from your classroom and the principal or vice principal is not in the building. Ask what you should do in this circumstance.

Here are two alternatives:

- Send student to the vice principal or school counselor.

- Send student to "time out" in another classroom.

With the prior consent of another teacher, a disruptive student is sent to a higher-grade classroom. When the student reaches the other classroom, she sits in a prearranged area away from the rest of the class. The student does not participate in the class activities and either sits quietly or does her own academic work.

Your administrator is an important part of your behavior management team. As such, he or she needs to be informed in advance of the involvement and support you expect. By introducing your discipline plan, you will assure your administrator that you are prepared to deal with student misbehavior on your own before asking for assistance. And by mutually establishing what action your administrator will take, you will help ensure that discipline problems will be handled in a fair and consistent manner by both of you.

Teach Your Classroom Discipline Plan to Your Students

A list of rules posted on your classroom wall is not enough to motivate students to always follow those rules. You must actively involve your students in the plan.

Teaching your classroom discipline plan to your students is as important as any lesson you will teach during the year. This lesson should take place the first day of school—and it must take place in every class that you teach.

The lesson should cover the following points:

1. Explain why you need rules.

2. Teach the rules.

3. Check for understanding.

4. Explain how you will reinforce students who follow the rules.

5. Explain why you have consequences.

6. Teach the consequences.

7. Check for understanding.

___

Here are some suggestions for teaching your lesson.

1 Discuss the need for rules.

First, make sure that all students understand why rules are needed in the classroom. Begin by discussing rules students are already familiar with at school and at home. Extend the discussion to include the need for laws in our community. Ask students to describe what a classroom, a home or a community would be like without such rules or laws.

2 Explain your classroom rules.

Now you must clearly explain each of your classroom rules. Talk about why each rule is necessary and why you have chosen it. For example, the rule "Be in your seat when the bell rings" is necessary to make sure that

lessons begin on time. By beginning lessons on time, you will be able to cover the material your students need to be successful in school.

3 Check for understanding.

Take the time to make sure that all students understand the rules you've taught. Ask if there are any questions about the rules. Have students repeat the rules to you in their own words. Above all, make sure that students understand that these rules are in effect at all times—during all activities.

4 Explain how you will reinforce students who follow the rules.

Positive reinforcement is going to be the most important part of your classroom discipline plan. Tell your students that you know they can all be successful at following the classroom rules, and that it will be your pleasure to recognize and reward those students who follow the rules. Pique student enthusiasm by detailing the positive reinforcement you will use.

> "See these 'You've Earned It!' coupons? From time to time I'll be giving these coupons to students who follow the rules and follow directions. I will be filling in the coupons with special privileges you would like to earn."

5 Explain why you have consequences.

Students need to understand that they are responsible for the behavioral choices they make.

> "By now, you may be wondering what will happen if you do not follow the rules. Let's talk about this for a moment.

> "Who can tell me what might happen at home if you broke an important rule? Would your parents restrict your use of the TV or phone? Why do your parents do this?

(Share responses.) Your parents want to help you learn to behave more responsibly.

"At school I want to help you learn to make responsible behavior choices. You need to know that when you choose to break a rule, something will happen—something you probably won't like very much."

6 Explain the consequences.

Tell students exactly what will happen if they choose to break a rule once in a day (or class period), twice, three times, four times and five times in a day or period. Explain how you will keep track of consequences.

(Hold up clipboard.) "I'm going to keep this clipboard near me throughout the class period. The first time you break a rule, I will write your name down. I'll also remind you of what the rule is. For example, if you throw a piece of crumpled paper across the room, all I will say to you is, 'Mike, the rule is keep feet, hands and objects to yourself. That is a warning.' If you are teasing another student, I'll say, 'Veronica, the rule is no teasing. That's a warning."

"That's all that I'll do.

"This warning gives you a second chance to choose appropriate behavior. Use this signal wisely so that you can avoid any further consequences.

"If you do break this rule again, or any other rule during the class period, I'll circle the '2' on the chart. This means that you've broken a rule two times, even if it's not the same rule, and that you have chosen to stay after class for one minute. I know one minute doesn't sound like a lot of time, but your friends will not be permitted to wait for you, and you will not be allowed to talk to anyone or move out of your seat until that minute is up. This will give you time to think about your behavior and plan to behave more appropriately in class.

"The third time you break a rule, you will stay after class for two minutes and complete a Behavioral Journal sheet which will be taken home and signed by your parent." (Give students a step-by-step explanation for completing the Behavior Journal sheet.)

Go through the rest of your hierarchy in this manner, explaining each consequence. Afterwards, take the time to emphasize your belief that the students can behave and make responsible choices for themselves.

"I know that all of you can follow our rules. I know that all of you can make good decisions when you enter the room, when you speak, when you do your work, and when you interact with your classmates. I hope that you won't have to experience disciplinary consequences, and that I won't have to call your parents or speak to the principal about problems. By making responsible choices you can make this your most successful and enjoyable year yet."

7 Check for understanding

It's important that all students clearly understand the consequences you will use. Ask students if they have any questions.

Keep this in mind: The manner in which you present your discipline plan to your students will set the tone for your classroom for the entire year. Be positive! Communicate your high expectations. Emphasize to your students that you believe they will choose to follow the rules and enjoy the rewards of their good behavior. However, students must also understand that if they choose to break a rule, a consequence will follow.

> *Refer to pages 97-110 of the revised Assertive Discipline text for additional sample scripts for teaching this lesson.*

It's Your Turn

Teaching your classroom discipline plan is an important lesson, one that will impact your classroom environment for the rest of the year. Take the time to carefully plan the lesson. Use the Lesson Planning Worksheet on the following pages as you organize your lesson.

TEACHING YOUR CLASSROOM DISCIPLINE PLAN

LESSON PLANNING WORKSHEET

1. Explain why you need rules in the classroom.

_____

_____

_____

_____

2. Explain the rules.

_____

_____

_____

_____

3. Check for understanding.

_____

_____

_____

_____

4. Explain how you will reinforce students who choose to follow the rules.

_____

_____

_____

_____

5. Explain why you have consequences.

_____

_____

_____

_____

_____

_____

6. Explain the consequences.

_____

_____

_____

_____

_____

_____

7. Check for understanding.

_____

_____

_____

_____

_____

_____

After you've taught the lesson . . .

Don't wait even one day, or one period, to start reinforcing students for following your classroom rules. As soon as the lesson has been taught, look for opportunities to recognize students for responsible behavior and immediately begin reinforcing students who follow the rules.

Let students know that you notice and appreciate the good efforts they're making. Through your actions let them know that you mean what you said about positive reinforcement.

"Amie, good job following my directions today."

"Richard, thank you for being in your seat before the bell rang."

It's Your Turn

The ideas that follow will help you reinforce students' appropriate behavior at the start of the year.

Student Express Card

Give students some extra credit for their good efforts! Reproduce one "Credit Card" (page 62) for each student. During a designated time period, such as a lecture or class discussion, ask students to leave their cards on their desks. Tell students that for the duration of the period, (discussion, lecture, lab work, etc.) you will be looking for students who are following directions and behaving responsibly. As you circulate the room, from time to time stamp or initial the cards of students who are behaving appropriately.

When all spaces on a student's card have been stamped or initialed, he or she turns in the card and earns a "You Deserve a Lot of Credit" reward coupon. These reproducible coupons (page 63) can be filled in by the teacher with a reward meaningful to the individual student.

Beginning-of-the-Year Awards

Good habits start early in the year! The awards on pages 64-65 are specially designed to recognize students who follow the rules at the start of the school year.

"Smart Start" Raffle Tickets

Reinforce good habits by awarding Smart Start Raffle Tickets to students who exhibit responsible behavior during the first weeks of school. When a student receives a ticket he or she signs and deposits it in the class collection box. Once a week a designated number of tickets are drawn and prizes or privileges given. This activity will motivate students to develop the responsible habits that will help them succeed all year long.

Post rules reminders.

On pages 67-70 you will find eye-catching posters of general rules that are commonly found in middle-school classrooms. If these rules are part of your plan, run them off on brightly colored paper (fluorescent or neon would get attention) and display them in the room.

An open-ended bordered poster is also included to use for other rules of your own, as well as a "Be Cool—Follow the Rules" poster that's applicable to any classroom.

Post your plan.

Display the Rules, Positive Recognition and Consequences posters (pages 11, 37 and 52) prominently in your classroom all year long.

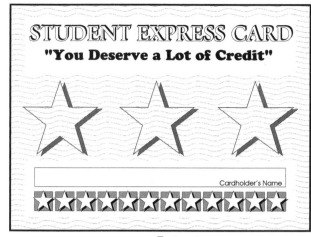

STUDENT EXPRESS CARD
"You Deserve a Lot of Credit"

Cardholder's Name

Congratulations on your super behavior!

This Student Express cardholder is entitled to

_____

_____

_____

Signed   Date

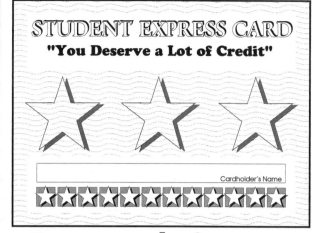

STUDENT EXPRESS CARD
"You Deserve a Lot of Credit"

Cardholder's Name

Congratulations on your super behavior!

This Student Express cardholder is entitled to

_____

_____

_____

Signed   Date

STUDENT EXPRESS CARD
"You Deserve a Lot of Credit"

Cardholder's Name

Congratulations on your super behavior!

This Student Express cardholder is entitled to

_____

_____

_____

Signed   Date

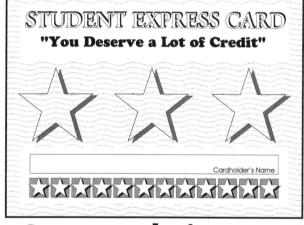

STUDENT EXPRESS CARD
"You Deserve a Lot of Credit"

Cardholder's Name

Congratulations on your super behavior!

This Student Express cardholder is entitled to

_____

_____

_____

Signed   Date

Congratulations,

_____!

You're off to a

Smart Start!

Thanks for following the rules!

_____
Signed   Date

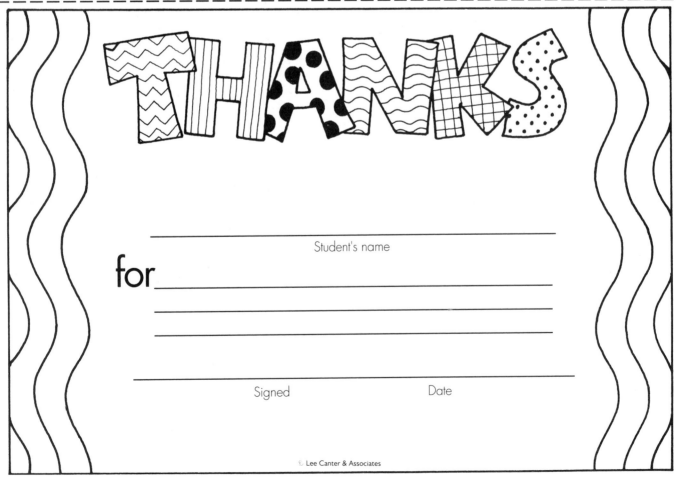

THANKS

for _____
Student's name

_____

_____

_____
Signed   Date

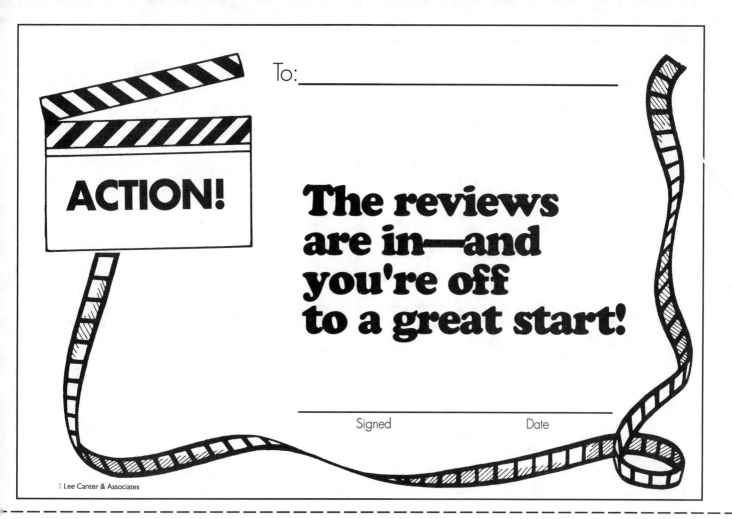

ACTION!

To:_____

**The reviews
are in—and
you're off
to a great start!**

_____ _____
Signed   Date

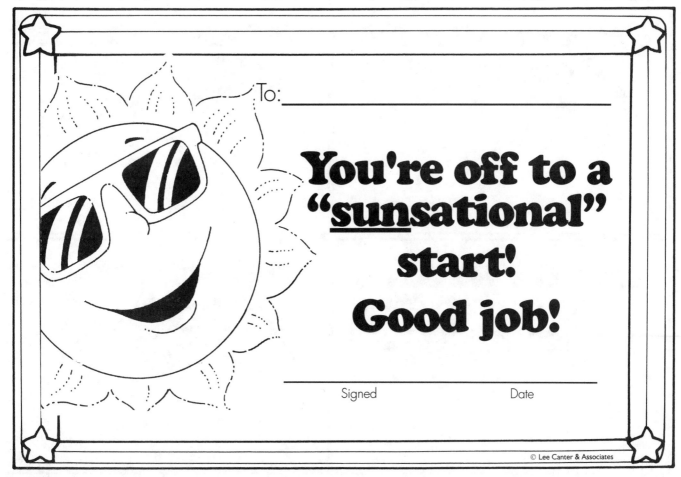

To:_____

**You're off to a
"<u>sun</u>sational"
start!
Good job!**

_____ _____
Signed   Date

SMART START
Raffle Ticket

NAME_____ Class/Period_____

SMART START
Raffle Ticket

NAME_____ Class/Period_____

SMART START
Raffle Ticket

NAME_____ Class/Period_____

SMART START
Raffle Ticket

NAME_____ Class/Period_____

SMART START
Raffle Ticket

NAME_____ Class/Period_____

SMART START
Raffle Ticket

NAME_____ Class/Period_____

SMART START
Raffle Ticket

NAME_____ Class/Period_____

SMART START
Raffle Ticket

NAME_____ Class/Period_____

CLASSROOM RULE

Follow directions.

CLASSROOM RULE

Keep hands, feet and objects to yourself.

CLASSROOM RULE

Do not leave the room without permission.

CLASSROOM RULE

Walk, don't run, in the classroom.

CLASSROOM RULE

Be Cool- Follow the Rules!

More Great Ideas!

Here are some ideas that will help you teach and reinforce your classroom discipline plan.

Create Student Behavior Folders

Have each student make a copy of the classroom discipline plan as it is posted. Each student then places this copy in his or her own Behavior Folder. (The folder can also be used to keep copies of specific directions as explained on page 87.) In a day or two, give a quick quiz on your classroom discipline plan. Tell students to use the information in their folders to study for the quiz.

Sample quiz questions:

- Write the four rules that are always in effect in our classroom.

- How many times a day do you receive a warning when you break a classroom rule?

- What happens the second time you break a rule?

For the record . . .

Record your first-of-the-year classroom discipline plan lesson on a cassette tape. Then when new students arrive in your classroom in mid year they won't be at a disadvantage— they can hear that all-important lesson first hand! Make sure that new students receive a copy of the discipline plan letter to take home to parents (see pages 74-75).

Send Home a Copy of Your Discipline Plan to Parents.

If parents are to become partners in their children's education, they must be well-informed about your classroom discipline plan. After all, contacting parents is part of your discipline hierarchy, and you want them to be supportive when you need them. Parents, therefore, need to be informed about why you have a plan and your rationale for rules, positive reinforcement and consequences.

Give each student a copy of your discipline plan to take home to parents. In a letter, explain why a classroom discipline plan is important, and ask parents to go over the plan with their children. Have parents and student sign and return a statement at the bottom that verifies that they have read the plan, discussed it together, and will support the plan. Keep the signed statements on file.

Tell your students:

"Before you leave today, each of you will receive a copy of this letter to your parents. This letter explains our classroom discipline plan. I want all of you to discuss the plan with your parents. After you have talked about the plan, I want you and your parents to sign the bottom of the sheet. Please bring the tear-off portion back to me. I want all of your parents to know what I expect of you in this class. And I want them to know that we will be working together to make sure this is a successful year for all of you."

Your letter to parents should include the following:

- Your reason for having a classroom discipline plan.

- A list of the rules, positive reinforcement and negative consequences that are included in your plan.

- A message asking parents to support your discipline plan.

- An invitation for parents to call you with any concerns they might wish to discuss.

- An acknowledgement statement to be signed by parent(s) and student.

- Space for comments.

Review your discipline plan with parents at Back-to-School Night. It's the perfect opportunity to discuss classroom rules, positive reinforcement and consequences, and to answer any questions parents may have.

It's Your Turn

Copy your discipline plan on the letterhead on page 76. Use the sample letter on page 75 as a guide for writing your own letter. Reproduce and distribute to parents. Make extra copies to keep on file for new students who enter your class during the school year.

Substitute Support

There will be times throughout the year when you won't be able to be at school—illness, meetings, etc. But you can make sure that your classes continue to run smoothly and productively—no matter who is in charge. To ensure consistent behavior management in your classroom, even when you are not present, prepare a discipline plan for substitutes. Fill in your discipline plan on the substitute's sheet on page 77. Make sure that a copy is left in the office. Put another copy in your lesson plan book or tape it to the top of your desk. If your plan is different in any respect for different classes, make sure you clearly designate this.

The rules of your classroom must be in effect at all times. Therefore, it is important that any paraprofessionals or volunteers who work in your room understand the discipline plan and the role they are to play in its implementation. Take time to explain the plan to your support staff. Make it very clear how they are to deal with both positive and negative behavior.

Classroom Plan

Dear Parent,

I am delighted that _____ is in my (social studies, English, math) class this year. With your encouragement, your child will participate in and enjoy many exciting and rewarding experiences this academic year.

Since lifelong success depends in part on learning to make responsible choices, I have developed a classroom discipline plan which guides every student to make good decisions about his or her behavior. Your child deserves the most positive educational climate possible for his/her growth, and I know that together we will make a difference in this process. The plan below outlines our rules, positive recognition for appropriate behavior and consequences for inappropriate behavior. They are:

Rules:
1. Follow directions.
2. Keep hands, feet and objects to yourself.
3. No swearing or teasing.

Positive Recognition:
To encourage students to follow these classroom rules, I will recognize appropriate behavior with praise, "good news" notes home and positive phone calls home.

Consequences:
If a student chooses to break a rule, however, the following steps will be taken:

First time a student breaks a rule:	Warning
Second time:	10 minutes working away from group
Third time:	15 minutes working away from group
Fourth time:	Call parents
Fifth time:	Send to principal
Severe Disruption:	Send to principal

Be assured that my goal is to work with you to ensure the success of your child this year. Please read and discuss this classroom discipline plan with your child, then sign and return the form below.

_____   _____   _____
Teacher's Signature   Class/Period   Date

— —

I have read the discipline plan and have discussed it with my child,_____.

Parent/Guardian Signature_____ Date_____

Student Signature_____

Comments:_____

_____

Classroom Plan

SUBSTITUTE'S PLAN

From the desk of: _____

Dear Substitute:

Listed below are the guidelines for the discipline plan used in my classroom. All of my students know the rules. They understand that these rules are in effect at all times, and they know the consequences that will occur should they break the rules of the classroom.

Please follow these guidelines exactly, and leave me a list of any students who break the rules.

Classroom Rules

1 _____
2 _____
3 _____
4 _____

Consequences

When a student breaks a rule:

1st time _____
2nd time _____
3rd time _____
4th time _____
5th time _____

Severe Clause: If a student exhibits severe misbehavior such as fighting, open defiance or vulgar language, the following consequence is to be immediately imposed: _____

Please offer plenty of praise and positive recognition to students who follow the rules. They'll appreciate it, and your praise will help encourage other students to cooperate, too!

Thank you for following my classroom discipline plan.

Sincerely,

Teaching Responsible Behavior

Developing your classroom discipline plan and teaching this plan to your students are the first steps you take to help them choose the responsible behavior that will enable them to succeed in school.

The next step is to teach your students how to make responsible behavioral choices in all situations at school.

In this section of the *Assertive Discipline Middle School Workbook* we will look at a variety of techniques that will help you motivate the majority of your students to behave appropriately.

Also included in this section is a selection of reproducibles that will help you implement these techniques.

Determining and Teaching Specific Directions

Your classroom discipline plan lists the general rules of your classroom. As you have seen, these rules are in effect at all times.

The most important of these classroom rules is, "Follow directions." This rule is included to ensure that students promptly follow *any* direction you might give during the day.

To comply with this rule, students must understand what each specific direction you give means. You can never assume that a classroom full of students will all follow a direction in the same way. After all, these students have 5 to 7 teachers each day—each with different procedures and routines to follow.

- Do your students know how you expect them to participate in a class discussion?

- Do they know how you expect them to transition from one activity to another?

- Do they know how you expect them to enter and leave the room?

There are many ways to go about following any direction. If you want all your students to follow a direction in the same way, you must teach them what you expect. Right at the beginning of the year you need to take the time to teach your students exactly how you want them to behave in all classroom situations. You need to teach and reteach your expectations until every student knows how to enter and leave the classroom, how to transition from one activity to another, and how to work in groups. Remember, the goal is for all of your students to succeed.

The more time you spend at the beginning of the year clarifying your specific directions, the less time you'll spend *repeating* them as the year goes by.

Here's what to do:

First, identify the academic activities, routine procedures and special procedures for which specific directions are needed.

Next, determine the specific directions you want your students to follow for each activity and procedure you've identified.

Here are examples of academic activities:

- When you are giving a directed lesson in front of the class

- When students are doing independent work

- When students are working in small groups doing cooperative learning tasks

- When the class is having a group discussion

- When students are taking a test

- When students are working at independent lab stations

- When a student is making a presentation to the class

- When students are engaged in sustained silent reading

Here are examples of routine procedures:

- When students enter the classroom
- When students are dismissed
- When a student needs to use the restroom
- When a student needs to sharpen a pencil
- When students turn in homework
- When the teacher gives a signal to begin an activity
- When students transition from one activity to another
- When the teacher is taking attendance
- When the phone rings or a PA announcement is heard
- When students are putting away equipment
- When students are cleaning up
- When students are viewing movies in class

Special Procedures

- When the fire drill bell rings
- When the class goes to a school assembly
- When guests come to the classroom
- When students are at the library
- Emergency procedures

  Note: Music teachers, art teachers, PE teachers and teachers who work in other special situations have to come up with a list of the activities and procedures that apply to their students.

For example:

- Putting music equipment away
- Putting sports equipment away
- Cleaning up after an art activity

The Difference Between Rules and Directions

- **Rules** are posted in your classroom, and are in effect at all times during the day.

- **Directions** are in effect for the duration of a specific activity. Directions may change based on the needs of the teacher and maturity level of the students.

It's Your Turn

Now think about a typical week in your own classroom. Start at the beginning of the school day on Monday and work your way through to the end of the day on Friday. Identify the academic activities, routine procedures and special procedures your students will be engaged in. Try not to leave anything out. List all of these on the Specific Directions Worksheet on page 82.

SPECIFIC DIRECTIONS WORKSHEET

Use this worksheet to list all the academic activities, routine procedures and special procedures that occur during the school week.

Academic Activities

- _____
- _____
- _____
- _____
- _____
- _____

- _____
- _____
- _____
- _____
- _____
- _____

Routine Procedures

- _____
- _____
- _____
- _____
- _____
- _____

- _____
- _____
- _____
- _____
- _____
- _____

Special Procedures

- _____
- _____
- _____
- _____
- _____
- _____

- _____
- _____
- _____
- _____
- _____
- _____

Now, determine the specific directions you want your students to follow.

After you've listed all the activities for which you need specific directions, it's time to decide on those directions. It's not as complicated as it might sound. When determining the specific directions you want your students to follow, use these guidelines:

- **Keep it simple!**
Choose a limited number of directions for each classroom activity.

- **Choose directions that are observable.**
Your directions must be observable and easy for students to follow. Don't include vague directions such as "act good" or "behave appropriately."

- **Relate your directions to:**
1 How you want students to participate in the activity or procedure—*what you expect them to do*.

2 How you expect students to *behave* in order to be successful in the activity.

Here are some examples of specific directions for a middle-school classroom:

Academic Activity: When the teacher is teaching a math lesson in front of the class

> **1** Clear your desks of everything but notebook and pencil. Have your notebook opened to the next clean sheet of paper.
>
> **2** Eyes on me, or eyes on your paper. No talking while I'm talking. No talking when another student is giving an answer or speaking.
>
> *(These directions let students know what they are expected to do.)*
>
> **3** Raise your hand and wait to be called upon to ask or answer a question. Don't shout out answers.
>
> *(This direction lets students know how you expect them to behave.)*

Academic Activity: When students are working independently

> **1** Have all necessary books, paper, pencils and other materials on your desk.
>
> **2** Begin working on your assignment as soon as you receive it.
>
> *(These directions let students know what they are expected to do.)*
>
> **3** No talking. Raise your hand to ask a question.
>
> *(This direction lets students know how you expect them to behave.)*

Routine Procedure: When students enter the classroom

> **1** Walk into the room.
>
> **2** Go directly to your seat and sit down.
>
> *(These directions let students know what they are expected to do.)*
>
> **3** No talking after the bell rings.
>
> *(This direction lets students know how you expect them to behave.)*

Special Procedure: Assemblies

> **1** Put books and materials away.
>
> **2** When your row (or section) is called, line up at the door in single file without talking. Remember to walk.
>
> **3** Without talking, walk to the cafeteria.
>
> **4** No talking during the assembly.
>
> **5** Return to class in a single line. No talking. Go directly to your seat and sit down.

It's Your Turn

Write the specific directions for the classroom activities that apply to your own teaching situation. We've started the list with some activities that generally take place in all classrooms. Add to this list as needed.

Activity: When students enter the classroom

1 _____

2 _____

3 _____

Activity: When you are giving a directed lesson

1 _____

2 _____

3 _____

Activity: When the class is involved in a class discussion

1 _____

2 _____

3 _____

Activity: When students are taking a test

1 _____

2 _____

3 _____

Activity: When students turn in homework

1 _____

2 _____

3 _____

Activity: When students leave the classroom at the end of the period

1 _____

2 _____

3 _____

Now write directions for any other classroom activities you listed on page 82.

Activity: _____

1 _____

2 _____

3 _____

Activity: _____

1 _____

2 _____

3 _____

Activity: _____

1 _____

2 _____

3 _____

Activity: _____

1 _____

2 _____

3 _____

Activity: _____

1 _____

2 _____

3 _____

Activity: _____

1 _____

2 _____

3 _____

Activity: _____

1 _____

2 _____

3 _____

Teach your specific directions.

Once you've determined your specific directions, your goal in teaching them is not to simply pass along instructions, but to make this process a learning experience for your students as well.

Teach students *why* your directions are important to cooperation and successful learning. When your students understand the need to follow directions, they can take ownership of the expectations you hold for the class and will be better able to meet those expectations.

Why teach specific directions with such care?

Here are two good reasons:

• Teaching your specific directions ensures that behavior problems will be reduced during all academic activities, routine procedures and special procedures.

• Teaching specific directions increases a student's opportunity to succeed at those activities.

As with any successful lesson, preparation is vital to meeting your objectives. The lesson sequence that follows highlights points you'll want to include in your own specific directions lessons. Use this lesson as a guideline for developing a lesson for any specific direction. Keep in mind that your own lessons will differ, based on the age and maturity of your students and the directions you are teaching, but the three main areas of focus—**explanation, teaching** and **checking for understanding**—remain the same.

Here's a sample lesson sequence for teaching the specific directions for silent reading:

1. Explain the rationale for the direction.
Students need to understand why your directions are important. Explain why students need to follow the direction and what the benefit will be to them and to other students.

"There will be times when you will be asked to read silently in class. Whether you are reading a newspaper article, a paragraph on a worksheet, or a chapter in your text, there are directions you must follow during silent-reading time. It's important to follow these directions so that you and your classmates will be able to complete the reading successfully and do well in class."

2. Involve the students by asking questions.
Students will follow your directions more readily if you involve them in a discussion that rationally addresses your concerns.

"What might happen if everyone did just what they wanted to do during silent-reading time?"

"Nicki, without directions, would you know what to do if you should finish reading before the other students?"

"What would happen if some of you decided to talk, get out of your seats or yell out a question while others were reading?"

"How could this effect everyone's ability to read silently? How could it effect your success in this class?"

3. Explain the specific directions.
Now teach students the directions they are to follow. Remind them that when everyone follows these directions, the negative outcomes that were discussed would not occur, disciplinary consequences wouldn't be necessary, and most importantly, all students would have an opportunity to succeed in class.

"These are the directions you need to follow whenever I give the direction to read silently in class:

"First, be sure that there are no objects in your hands or on your desk other than the book or paper from which you are reading.

"Begin reading as soon as you are given the direction. No talking or making noise. Stay in your seat and keep your chair on 'all fours.'

"If you get stuck on a word or have a question about the reading, raise your hand. I will come to your desk and assist you or ask you to come to my desk."

"When you have finished reading, just sit quietly and think about what you have read, or you may do some rereading of the assignment. Be prepared to discuss what you've read."

4. Check for understanding.

Check for understanding by asking students to restate the directions. Then reinforce the directions further by writing them on the board or presenting them on an overhead. At this point you may also want to have students copy the specific directions and add them to their Behavior Folders (see page 73).

"Raise your hand if you can tell me the directions you need to follow when asked to read silently."

After you've taught a specific directions lesson . . .

Immediately follow up any specific directions lesson with the activity or procedure that has just been taught. (In the previous example, the teacher would actually then give students a silent-reading assignment.) Be sure to reinforce students who follow the directions appropriately, and give reminders to (or reteach if necessary) those students who are having difficulty.

"Good, Mai! You began reading as soon as I gave the direction."

"Felipe, you're in your seat with all four legs of your chair on the floor. Great job!"

"Margo and Candace, you remembered to sit quietly after you finished reading."

Guidelines for Reviewing Specific Directions

First Two Weeks
Review directions each time the class engages in the activity.

First Month
Review directions each Monday (as a reminder and refresher for the week to come).

Remainder of Year
Review directions as needed. It is especially important to review directions after a vacation, on special days when students are excited (field trips, day before a vacation, the day of a class party, dance or big game).

Refer to pages 128-136 of the revised Assertive Discipline text for additional guidelines for teaching specific directions to your students.

It's Your Turn

Here are some ideas that will help you teach specific directions to your students:

Plan your lessons.

Use the Specific Directions Planning Sheet on the next two pages to plan the lessons you will teach. Make plenty of copies and use them to write down questions you want to ask students during the lesson, points you want to make, and other reminders to yourself.

Post your directions.

Visual reminders can often help students remember directions. Use the open-ended poster on page 91 to create handy reminders of some of your more commonly given (or most important) directions.

Recognize students who follow directions.

Encourage students to "letter" in good behavior! The reproducible notes on pages 92-94 will help you recognize students who follow directions. (The awards are open-ended so they can be used any time you want to praise a student—for any reason!)

Create a Classroom Directions Binder

As new students enter your class throughout the year, they too will need to learn your specific directions. Here's an idea that can help ease their transition and involve peers in the teaching process:

Use the "Directions for _____" worksheet on page 91 to create a list of directions for different activities. Organize these sheets into a looseleaf binder. When a new student joins the class, assign him or her a buddy or guide. It's the responsibility of the guide to go through the binder with the new student and explain each of these directions.

The binder can also be used to reteach students who repeatedly receive warnings or consequences for not following directions. Have the student read and copy the directions he or she is having trouble with to help reinforce understanding of the directions.

LESSON PLAN FOR TEACHING
SPECIFIC DIRECTIONS

Objective: To teach specific directions for_____

When to present this lesson: Teach directions for this activity prior to the first
time the activity takes place.

These are the specific directions I will teach for this activity.

_____

_____

_____

_____

_____

Now, plan the lesson you will teach.

Explain the rationale for the direction:

_____

_____

_____

_____

_____

_____

_____

_____

_____

_____

_____

_____

_____

_____

_____

_____

_____

Involve the students by asking questions:

_____
_____
_____
_____
_____
_____
_____

Explain the specific directions:

_____
_____
_____
_____
_____
_____

Check for understanding:

_____
_____
_____
_____

Notes on the lesson:

_____
_____
_____
_____
_____
_____
_____

DIRECTIONS for

SENSATIONAL!

Thanks, _____ ,
for _____
_____
_____
_____

SENSATIONAL!

Thanks, _____ ,
for _____
_____
_____
_____

UNIQUE!

Thanks, _____ ,
for _____
_____
_____
_____

UNIQUE!

Thanks, _____ ,
for _____
_____
_____
_____

PHENOMENAL!

Thanks, _____ ,
for _____
_____
_____
_____

PHENOMENAL!

Thanks, _____ ,
for _____
_____
_____
_____

EXCEPTIONAL!

Thanks, _____ ,
for _____
_____
_____
_____

EXCEPTIONAL!

Thanks, _____ ,
for _____
_____
_____
_____

REMARKABLE!   REMARKABLE!

Thanks, _____ ,

for _____

_____

_____

_____

Thanks, _____ ,

for _____

_____

_____

_____

Teaching Responsible Behavior
Using Positive Recognition to Motivate Students to Behave

Once you've taught your students directions for all classroom activities, your goal is to help them be successful in following those directions.

Positive recognition is the most effective way to achieve this goal.

We will give you a variety of techniques that you can use to motivate students to choose appropriate behavior and then to *continue* that behavior.

These techniques are:

1 Positive Repetition

2 Consistent Praise

3 Scanning

4 Circulating the Classroom

On the following pages you will learn how to use each of these techniques throughout the day—while you teach, and while you are involved in any classroom activity.

These reproducible Cue Cards give you portable, to-the-point references for successfully handling both appropriate and inappropriate classroom behavior.

Here are some guidelines for using the Cue Cards:

- **Read**

Read each Cue Card. Take time to think about how you can use each of these techniques in the day-to-day routine of your classroom.

- **Keep**

Laminate the Cue Cards and then tuck them into your lesson plan book for easy reference. From time to time review the techniques and make sure you are using them—effectively *and* consistently.

- **Share**

Give a set of Cue Cards to your classroom aide or to parent volunteers. Encourage them to read the cards and use the techniques with students.

Keep positive recognition techniques at your fingertips with Assertive Discipline Cue Cards.

What are Assertive Discipline Cue Cards?

Cue Cards are a quick and easy way to keep Assertive Discipline techniques close at hand and in your mind. All of the positive recognition techniques listed in this chapter, and other behavior management techniques included in upcoming chapters, have been organized into easy-to-use Assertive Discipline Cue Cards.

ASSERTIVE DISCIPLINE in Action!

Positive Repetition

This technique will help encourage students to follow the many directions you give each day. It's called positive repetition.

Here's how positive repetition works:

1 Give a direction.

2 Immediately look for at least two students who are following the direction.

3 Say the students' names and restate the direction as they are following it.

Examples:

Direction:
"Please take out your science notebooks."
Positive Repetition:
"Toni and Spencer have their notebooks out and are ready for our lesson."

Direction:
"Please move into your math groups."
Positive Repetition:
"Patty's in her group area. That was very fast! Howard is in his place, too!"

CUE CARD # 1

Guidelines for Frequency of Positive Repetition

At the beginning of the year you will be placing a heavy emphasis on teaching students how to behave. The more you want to teach children how to behave, the more you need to use praise. Thus, at the beginning of the year you will use positive repetition much more frequently than you will once your students learn what you need them to do in each classroom situation. Remember, one of the goals of positive reinforcement is to start strong, then gradually decrease the frequency.

Weeks 1-2	Use positive repetition every time you give a direction. Don't worry about overdoing it.
Weeks 2-4	Use positive repetition every third time you give a direction.
After first month:	Use positive repetition every fourth time you give a direction. Maintain this frequency level throughout the year.

Positive repetition is a positive advantage for you and your students!

You give hundreds of directions in a week. And each time you give a direction you have a ready-made opportunity to positively reinforce students. When you get into the habit of using this technique, you will be assured that you will make more positive than negative statements to students.

ASSERTIVE DISCIPLINE
in Action!

Consistent Praise

An effective way to encourage students to continue their appropriate behavior is to continually monitor the class—even while teaching—and provide frequent praise and positive support to those students who are on task.

Keep these guidelines in mind:

Effective praise is personal.

Always include the student's name. A statement like "Thank you for working quietly" is not as meaningful as "Kara and Jessica, thank you for working quietly."

Note: Remember that some middle-school students do not respond well to praise given in front of their peers. With these students it is best to deliver praise quietly after class or unobtrusively during a transition.

Effective praise must be genuine.

To be convincing to students, to show that you really mean what you say, be genuinely appreciative of their appropriate behavior.

Effective praise is descriptive and specific.

When praising students, be specific. That way, students will know exactly what they did to deserve the praise and will be more likely to repeat those behaviors. For example:

Descriptive Praise	Vague Praise
"Thanks, Sue, for an exciting presentation."	"Way to go, Sue."
"You must have really studied for this history test, Mark."	"Nice job, Mark."
"Thank you for putting the books away, Sara."	"I like the way you're helping, Sara."

CUE CARD # 2

ASSERTIVE DISCIPLINE
in Action!

Scanning

The scanning technique is useful when you are working with a small group of students, or an individual student, and the rest of the class is working independently. The objective of this technique is to reinforce students who are on task, thereby encouraging them to remain on task. This technique will help you recognize students who normally may not receive attention until they misbehave. By using this technique, you can keep independent workers on task and still remain working with one small group.

Here's how to use the scanning technique:

1 When you are working with a small group, look up every few minutes and scan the students who are working independently.

2 As you notice students who are working appropriately, take a moment to recognize their good behavior.

"Robert is working quietly on his social studies assignment. Thank you, Robert."

3 The student will appreciate the recognition and continue working independently. Other students will get the message that you are aware of what's going on in the room, and will be motivated to stay on task themselves.

CUE CARD # 3

ASSERTIVE DISCIPLINE
in Action!

Circulating the Classroom

While students are working independently, circulate the room and give positive recognition. One-on-one, you can let a student know that you recognize his or her appropriate behavior. This positive recognition is given quietly—a special message from the teacher to the student.

"Sofia, you've done a great job on your history questions. You finished the entire assignment!"

"Carl, you've been very cooperative today. You are really trying hard to get along with everyone."

There is no need to ever phase out this technique. Each time you circulate the classroom you have an opportunity to show your students you care, and that you notice their good efforts.

CUE CARD # 4

Teaching Responsible Behavior
Redirecting Non-disruptive Off-task Behavior

By giving your students consistent positive recognition, you can eliminate the majority of problems before they even begin.

Experience has perhaps shown you, however, that there still will be students who behave inappropriately. This behavior can take two forms: disruptive off-task behavior and non-disruptive off-task behavior.

Disruptive Off-task Behaviors

Shouting out in class

Throwing spit balls

Pushing or shoving

Running in the classroom

Non-disruptive Off-task Behaviors

Looking out the window

Reading instead of listening

Doodling instead of working

Daydreaming

We will take a closer look at disruptive off-task behavior, and how to deal with it, on pages 107-108. Now we will focus on how to respond to non-disruptive off-task behavior—behavior in which a student is not disrupting others, but is not paying attention or staying on task, either.

As any teacher knows, students frequently fall into non-disruptive off-task behavior. After all, it doesn't take much for a sixth grader to lose interest in class and start doodling on his paper, or for a seventh grader to stare out the window instead of listening to a lecture.

The teacher's responsibility is to guide the student back into learning.

Here's what you *don't* want to do:

1) ignore the behavior or

2) give an immediate consequence.

Ignoring the behavior doesn't get the student back on task, and therefore the student isn't participating or learning.

Giving an immediate consequence in many cases is an overreaction to a simple lapse of attention.

Here's what you *do* want to do:

Calmly, and with caring guidance, give the student an opportunity to get back on task.

It's Your Turn

The Assertive Discipline Cue Cards on pages 103-106 contain four techniques that will help you redirect a student's non-disruptive off-task behavior *while you teach*. Read each technique and imagine how you can use it throughout the day to nudge students back into your lessons. Reproduce these Cue Cards, laminate them, and keep them nearby for easy and frequent review.

1 The Look

2 Physical Proximity

3 Mention Name

4 Proximity Praise

Once a student is back on track?

As soon as a student is back on task, take advantage of the opportunity to praise his or her behavior. Let the student know that paying attention in class earns positive recognition.

How often do you redirect?

How many times should you redirect students before you start giving consequences? Obviously you can't go on redirecting a student over and over within a class period. At some point you may have to turn to consequences.

Here's a rule of thumb:

When you find yourself having to redirect a student twice in a period you can assume that the student is not receiving enough structure to help him control his behavior. In these situations, turn to your disciplinary hierarchy and issue a warning.

If the off-task behavior still continues, you may need to proceed further and use consequences from your disciplinary hierarchy.

> Note: If the non-disruptive off-task behavior seems out of character for a student, something might be wrong that you need to know about. Before turning to consequences, take the student aside and, in a caring manner, say (for example), "It seems like it's hard for you to pay attention in class today. Would you like to talk about it?"

Always remember that your own good judgment is your most valuable guide in assessing student behavior.

The "Look"

Just giving a look that says "I'm aware of and disapprove of your behavior" is an effective way of redirecting non-disruptive off-task behavior.

Here's how this technique works:

Instead of attentively listening to a social studies lesson, Karen aimlessly sits tipping her chair back on two legs. When the teacher notices Karen's off-task behavior, she makes direct eye contact with her and looks at her with a firm, calm look on her face. She maintains this eye contact until Karen puts all four legs of her chair on the floor and begins to take notes.

CUE CARD # 5

ASSERTIVE DISCIPLINE *in Action!*

Physical Proximity

Sometimes you don't even have to say a word to redirect a student back on task. Simply walk over and stand close by the student. The student will know why you've arrived at his or her side and will respond.

Here's an example of physical proximity at work:

While reading a story to the class, the teacher notices that Danny has put his head down on his desk and has "tuned out." Continuing to read, the teacher walks back to Danny's desk and stands near his desk while she proceeds with the story. Danny notices her presence, lifts his head and starts paying attention.

CUE CARD # 6

ASSERTIVE DISCIPLINE *in Action!*

Mention the off-task student's name while teaching.

Just mentioning a student's name while you are teaching a lesson may be enough to redirect his or her attention back on task.

Here's an example of a teacher using this technique:

While at the board teaching a math lesson, the teacher notices that Clarice is off task and not paying attention. The teacher, in a matter-of-fact manner, continues the lesson saying, "All right, for our next problem let's say that Clarice is planning to fly from Portland, Oregon to Los Angeles, California—a distance of 1100 miles. If the flight takes two hours . . . ."

As soon as Clarice's name is mentioned, she looks up, tunes in, and immediately begins paying attention.

CUE CARD # 7

Proximity Praise

An effective way to redirect a non-disruptive off-task student back on task is to focus on the appropriate *behavior of those students around him.*

Here's an example of a teacher using proximity praise:

The entire class, with the exception of Jason, is working independently on their assignments. Rather than doing his assignment, Jason is idly doodling pictures in his notebook. On either side of Jason, Colleen and Jeff are both doing their work. Wanting to get Jason on task, the teacher says, "Colleen and Jeff are doing an excellent job on their assignments."

As she expects, Jason looks around him, notices what is going on and gets back to work.

This technique is doubly effective. Off-task students are motivated to get back on task, and students who are on task receive well-deserved praise.

CUE CARD # 8

Implementing Consequences

We have talked about the importance of middle-school students learning to accept responsibility for the behavior choices they make. As part of this learning, students need to understand that negative consequences are a natural outcome of misbehavior.

When students disrupt and keep you from teaching, or other students from learning, you will have to follow through with consequences.

On page 45 you learned to develop a discipline hierarchy as part of your classroom discipline plan. How you use the consequences in the hierarchy will determine its success in helping you motivate students to choose responsible behavior.

Remember, the key is not the consequences themselves, but the inevitability that they will occur each time a rule is broken or a direction is not followed—not sometimes, not every now and then, but every single time.

Students will not respect your praise unless it is backed up with firm limits, and limits will be ineffective unless staying within those limits is backed up by praise.

Follow these guidelines to ensure that your use of disciplinary consequences will help students choose responsible behavior.

1. Provide consequences in a calm, matter-of-fact manner.

One of the benefits of a discipline hierarchy is that you always know how you will react to student misbehavior. Because you've *planned* how to deal with misbehavior, you will be able to give consequences calmly, without anger and with the assuredness that the consequence is both appropriate and fair.

> "Steven, this is the second time I've had to speak to you about calling out in class. You have chosen to wait after class for one minute."

2. Be consistent. Provide a consequence every time a student chooses to disrupt.

As we have pointed out, it is the consistency of consequences that is the key to their effectiveness.

3. After a student receives a consequence, find the first opportunity you can to recognize positive behavior.

After a consequence has been given, teachers often continue to focus on that student's negative behavior—just waiting for the student to "act up" again. This may be a natural response, but it does little to encourage a student to choose more appropriate behavior.

Don't look for negative behavior. Instead, take the first opportunity to recognize the student's *appropriate* behavior. Your role in providing behavioral guidance to your students (not punishment) means that you must communicate the high expectations you have for each student's success.

Again, use discretion in how you recognize a student for appropriate behavior. Sometimes a simple smile or thumbs up from across the room can convey as much as a verbal acknowledgment.

4. Provide an "escape mechanism" for students who are upset and want to talk about what happened.

After receiving a consequence, students will often want you to stop what you are doing and listen to their side of the story.

The following "escape mechanisms" will let students diffuse their anger and "get something off their chest" without disrupting the rest of the class:

* Have the student write you a note that you will discuss with him or her after class or when you have a break in the lesson.

- Use a notebook to record misbehavior that allows space for students to write their comments.

- Have students keep a daily journal or diary in which they can record any comments.

5. When a student continuously disrupts, "move in."

There may be times when a student will continue to disrupt even after he or she has been given a warning or a consequence. In these situations, a technique called "moving in" (see Cue Card #9 on the next page) will often effectively stop disruptive behavior.

Keep in mind that by providing consequences calmly and consistently, you will effectively help most students choose responsible behavior, and stop most disruptive behavior in your classroom. In spite of these efforts, however, there are going to be some cases in which students will challenge your authority and confront you. When a student tries to manipulate you or argue with you, you must stay in charge and refocus the conversation. Refer to the refocusing technique on Cue Card #10 (page 110) for specific guidelines.

> *Refer to pages 169-186 of the revised Assertive Discipline text for sample scenarios demonstrating teachers effectively using consequences in a variety of teaching situations.*

"Moving In"

Many times physical proximity is all that is needed to help calm down a student and stop the disruptive behavior. Here's an effective technique to use when a student is being disruptive in class:

1 Move close to the student.

Walk over to the student. Get close. Show your concern and in a quiet, firm manner let the student know that his or her behavior is inappropriate.

2 In a caring manner, remind the student of the consequences received so far, and what will happen next if the misbehavior continues.

"Monica, I am concerned that your behavior today is going to result in consequences that you don't really want. You've been doing such a good job all week. I'm proud of the work you've done and I'd like to see it continue. Now you've received a warning and two consequences. One more disruption and I will be calling your parents tonight. Do you understand?"

With older students, "move out."

With older students, it may be more appropriate to "move out" of the classroom to speak to the student. Removing the audience of peers may increase the effectiveness of your limit-setting efforts.

When you "move out," remember to:
- stay calm.
- avoid arguing with the student.
- recognize the student's feelings.

CUE CARD # 9

ASSERTIVE DISCIPLINE in Action!

Refocusing an argumentative conversation

When a student starts arguing with you, you must stay in charge. Do not get involved in an argument. Do not let the student pull you into a pointless exchange. Instead, stay in control, refocus the conversation and help get the student back on task.

Here's what to do:

- Stay calm.

- State what you want: "I want you to sit down and do your assignment."

- Preface your statement of want with understanding for the student.

- Repeat your statement of want a maximum of three times. If the student still argues, let her know that she may be choosing to receive a consequence.

Here's an example of a teacher using the refocusing technique with a disruptive student:

Teacher: *(calmly but firmly)* Bonnie, I want you to sit down and get to work on your assignment.

Bonnie: It's almost done. I'll finish it tonight. I need to talk to Michelle about our report for Mr. Johnson's class. We'll be quiet. We won't bother anyone.

Teacher: I understand, Bonnie, but I want you to sit down and do your work for this class.

Bonnie: But I need to talk to Michelle. It's important. Why are you making such a big deal out of this?

Teacher: Bonnie, I see that you're upset, but sit down and begin your work.

Bonnie: I'm just trying to get my work done. It's due tomorrow.

Teacher: Bonnie, if you do not get to work immediately, you and I will call your mother during lunch. The choice is yours.

CUE CARD # 10

Difficult Students

Consistent use of the classroom management skills presented in the first part of this workbook will enable most teachers to teach 90-95% of their students to choose responsible behavior.

The remaining 5 to 10%—the difficult students you sometimes encounter—are the focus of this section, in which we will cover four aspects of dealing successfully with difficult students:

- One-to-One Problem-Solving Conferences

- Using Positive Support to Build Positive Relationships

- Developing an Individualized Behavior Plan

- Getting Support from Parents and Administrators

One-to-One Problem-Solving Conferences

A one-to-one problem-solving conference is a meeting between you and your student to discuss a *specific* behavior problem. The goal of this conference is not to punish but to listen to the student and give caring and firm guidance. This conference should be looked upon as a cooperative effort on the student's behalf.

How do you know when a one-to-one conference is needed?

Ask yourself, "If this were my child, would I want the teacher to sit down and work with her to help improve her behavior? Would I want the teacher to take the time and interest to show my child better options?"

If the answer is yes, then it is time to meet with the student.

Keep these guidelines in mind when conducting a one-to-one problem-solving conference:

1 Show empathy and concern.
First and foremost, let the student know that you are concerned and that you care about him or her. Let the student know that you are meeting not to punish but to help and offer guidance.

2 Question the student to find out why there is a problem.
Don't assume you know why the student is misbehaving. Ask questions.

> "Did something happen today to get you so upset?"

> "Are other students bothering you?"

> "Do you have trouble seeing the board?"

> "Is the work too difficult for you?"

> "Is something happening at home or in your neighborhood that's causing problems?"

3 Determine what you can do to help.
Is there anything you can do to help solve the problem? There may in fact be a simple answer that you don't want to overlook.

For example:

- If a student is having trouble in class with another student, move his seat.

- If a disruptive student is seated at the back of the class, consider moving her forward.

- Contact the parents if you feel the student needs additional help and support from home.

- Increase your positive attention toward the student, not just your consequences. Look for the first praiseworthy behavior after the conference, offer words of praise and send a positive note home.

- A student may need academic help that you, a tutor or a peer study buddy may be able to provide. Make that help available.

4 Determine how the student can improve his or her behavior.
Ask the student for his or her input concerning ways to improve the problem behavior. Share ideas. Keep in mind that some students may not be willing or able to share their feelings about choosing different behavior. If this is the case, help them by pointing out more appropriate behavior.

5 Agree on a course of action.
Combine your input with the student's input and agree upon a plan of action both of you can follow to improve the situation.

6 Clearly state to the student that you expect him to change his behavior.

At some point during the conference you must let the student know that you expect behavior to improve.

> "I'm going to work with you to solve this problem, Jimmy. You're a smart student and I know you can behave responsibly. But you have to remember that fighting is not allowed at our school. Anytime you fight you will be choosing to go to the principal."

7 Summarize the conference. Show your confidence!

Wrap up the conference by summarizing what was said. Most important, end with a note of confidence.

> "I think we made a good start today. I know you can do better. Starting tomorrow, it will be different. I'm glad we had this talk."

Keep in mind that middle-school students do not want to be *told* what to do. They want to feel they have a say in how they choose to behave. Whenever possible, involve the student in discussing how he or she should change behavior. Listen carefully to the student's input and give credence to his or her thoughts.

Please refer to pages 207-216 of the Assertive Discipline text for examples of scripted one-to-one problem–solving conferences.

It's Your Turn

Use the Problem-Solving Conference Worksheet on page 114 as a guide for conducting the conference and as a record of what was accomplished at the conference. If parents need to be involved at a future date, you will have documentation of steps already taken to solve the problem.

PROBLEM-SOLVING CONFERENCE
WORKSHEET

Student's name _____ Date _____

1. Problem behavior the student is having (reason for conference):

_____

_____

_____

2. Student input regarding problem (Why does the student think this problem is occurring?):

_____

_____

3. Steps the teacher can take to help solve the problem:

_____

_____

_____

4. Actions the student can take to solve the problem:

_____

_____

_____

5. Course of action agreed upon between teacher and student:

_____

_____

_____

_____

_____

Follow-up and Notes:

_____

_____

_____

_____

_____

Using Positive Support to Build Positive Relationships

The middle–school years are often stressful for students. Their lives are filled with constant change as they begin to leave childhood behind and experience the tumultuous physical, psychological and social changes that mark the entry into adulthood.

Middle-school teachers, therefore, fill a very special role in students' lives. Quite simply, they are the guides through some of the most difficult years a young person will encounter. And for many students, their teachers are the most positive, caring role models they will have.

It is extremely important, then, that you make a special effort to establish positive relationships with difficult students—relationships that demonstrate your caring commitment to their success and well being. Show these students that you care about them as unique individuals and that you are deeply concerned about their behavior.

In order to successfully raise the self-esteem of a difficult student, you may have to go beyond your daily program of praise and positive reinforcement. Use special approaches and activities that enable you to reach out to those students on an individual basis to build a strong, positive relationship.

It's as simple as this: Treat students the way you would want your own child to be treated in school.

It's Your Turn

The following pages contain ideas for fostering and building positive relationships with difficult students—Student Interest Inventory, Teacher Interest Inventory and an Assertive Discipline Cue Card detailing effective techniques to use with difficult students.

Discover Your Students' Interests

In order to establish personal relationships with your students, you need to learn about their likes and dislikes, interests and goals. A Student Interest Inventory, taken at the beginning of the year, is a great way to learn more about each student. Explain to your students that this inventory will help you become better acquainted with each of them. Make this inventory (page 116) the first homework assignment of the year. Keep a supply of Student Interest Inventories on hand throughout the year to give to transfer students entering your classroom. The information you gather could be the building blocks of a positive student/teacher relationship.

Turnabout is fair play!

Don't forget, students will want to know something about you, too. Create a Teacher Interest Inventory detailing your likes and dislikes, interests and goals. (Use the reproducible on page 117.) Distribute a copy of the completed inventory to each student. Encourage students to discuss the inventory with you. Getting to know each other will help you build trusting relationships with students.

More Ideas for Building Positive Relationships

Build strong, positive relationships with difficult students by incorporating the simple, yet effective techniques found on Assertive Discipline Cue Card #11 into your daily routine. Keep this card handy as a reminder of the many ways you can make positive contact with all students, especially difficult ones, throughout the day.

> *Please refer to pages 217-226 of the Assertive Discipline text for additional suggestions for building positive relationships with students.*

STUDENT INTEREST INVENTORY

Name _____

Brothers and Sisters
Name _____ Age _____
Name _____ Age _____
Name _____ Age _____
Name _____ Age _____

Special friends:

_____ _____ _____

_____ _____ _____

What I like to do most at home: _____

_____

These are my favorite hobbies: _____

_____

These are my favorites:
book: _____ TV show: _____
movie: _____ food: _____
singer: _____ song: _____

If I had one wish, I would want to: _____

_____

School would be better if: _____

_____

If I had a million dollars, I would: _____

_____

This is what my teacher did last year that I liked the most: _____

_____

This is what my teacher did last year that I liked the least: _____

_____

_____

TEACHER INTEREST INVENTORY

Name _____

Family (optional):

Spouse _____

Children (ages) _____

Brothers and sisters? _____

What I like to do most at home: _____
_____
_____

These are my favorite hobbies: _____
_____
_____

This is my favorite book: _____

This is my favorite TV show: _____

This is my favorite movie: _____

This is my favorite performer: _____

If I had one wish, I would want to: _____
_____
_____

If I had a million dollars, I would: _____
_____

What I like best about middle-school students: _____
_____

What I like best about teaching: _____
_____
_____

Why I became a teacher: _____
_____
_____

ASSERTIVE DISCIPLINE *in Action!*

Ideas for Using Positive Support to Build Positive Relationships

• Greet your students at the door.

Start each day with a smile and a personal greeting—for each and every student. Stand at the door as your students enter the room and greet each student by name. "Good morning, Johnny. Nice to see you, Sally. Hi, Jeff." This is an especially effective way to make personal, positive contact with those students who need your individual attention and caring words.

• Spend a few special minutes with students who need your one-to-one attention.

The most precious and valuable gift you can give difficult students is your undivided attention. Take a few minutes during class, at recess, during lunch or after school to talk with the student. Share information about yourself. Inquire about the student's feelings and concerns. Let that student know that you are there to offer assistance, understanding and a sympathetic ear when necessary.

• Make home visits.

One very effective way to gain insight into a difficult student's behavior is to visit that student and his or her family at their home. Getting acquainted on this neutral ground is a great way to build positive relationships with difficult students and their families. Prearrange a home visit with the family. At the meeting inquire about their concerns and goals for the school year. Share your plans.

• Make a phone call after a difficult day.

End a difficult day on a positive note by phoning a student with a positive message about tomorrow. Discuss any difficulties that occurred during the day. Get student input. Most important, your phone call should emphasize your confidence that these problems can be worked through and that tomorrow both of you can start fresh.

• Make a positive phone call when a student has had a good day.

What better way to let a student know that he or she is on the right track than by making a quick phone call to offer some well-earned words of praise. If the student isn't home, share the good news with parents and have them deliver the positive message later.

• Make get-well calls.

When a student is ill, pick up the phone and call to find out how the child is feeling. Both parents and student will appreciate your caring and concern.

CUE CARD # 11

Developing an Individualized Behavior Plan

When your general classroom discipline plan is not effective with a student, you'll need to establish an individualized behavior plan for him or her. Such a plan is designed to adapt the elements of your regular classroom discipline plan to meet the unique needs of a particular student.

An individualized behavior plan can help teach the student to behave responsibly and help you to develop the positive relationship with that student that so far may have been out of reach.

An individualized behavior plan includes:

• The specific behaviors expected of the student.

• Meaningful consequences to be imposed if the student does not choose to engage in the appropriate behavior.

• Meaningful positive recognition to be given when the student does behave appropriately.

Guidelines for developing an individualized behavior plan:

1 Determine the behavior(s) you expect from the student.

Select only one or two behaviors to work on at a time. Choose those that you believe are most important to the student's success. For example, if a student has a consistent problem with staying in his seat, the rule "Stay in your seat unless told to get up" would be an appropriate behavior to target.

2 Decide on meaningful consequences.

Often you will find that a difficult student reaches the same consequence on the discipline hierarchy each day. For example, a student might reach the third step on the

hierarchy every day and stay after class for two minutes on each of those days.

First disruption: Warning

Second disruption: One minute after class

Third disruption: Two minutes after class

Fourth disruption: Contact parents

Fifth disruption: Send student to principal

Conclusion? It appears in this case that the student does not really mind staying after class all that much and thus the consequence is not effective.

If you look at it in another way, you will note that the student *always* stops short of the consequence that involves calling the parent. In this case the teacher can conclude that it may be effective to individualize this student's discipline plan so that the first time she disrupts, instead of a warning or staying after class, her parents are immediately contacted.

For example:

First disruption: Call parents

Second disruption: Send student to principal

> Note: It may be appropriate with some difficult students to provide consequences that are not on your regular classroom discipline hierarchy. It may be necessary, for example, to keep a student in at lunch or after school even though those consequences are not on your hierarchy.

Keep in mind that no matter what the consequence is, it must always be one that will be meaningful to the student and, as always, provided consistently each time the student chooses to misbehave.

3 Determine more meaningful positive recognition.

Your firmer, more meaningful consequences must always be balanced with increased positive recognition. As always, your positive recognition should begin with praise. Once you have implemented an individualized behavior plan, look for every opportunity to recognize the student's appropriate behavior. Make it a point to genuinely praise the student several times a day.

Back up your praise with other forms of positive recognition that you feel are appropriate, such as positive notes home or special privileges.

Keep parents informed.

A parent's involvement in an individualized behavior plan is critical. After all, it is likely that "Call Parents" may be the first consequence given. Whenever you establish an individualized plan for a student, personal contact with the parent is vital. A phone call or face-to-face meeting is your best means of communicating the plan.

Here are the points you will want to cover in the meeting:

1. Emphasize to the parents that your goal in establishing the individualized plan is to help the student learn more responsible behavior that will allow him or her to succeed in school.

2. Explain the one or two behaviors that you are dealing with in the plan. Let the parents know why you have chosen to emphasize these behaviors.

3. Tell the parents what will happen the first time the student breaks one of these rules. Explain why you have chosen these "more meaningful" consequences.

4. Tell the parents what will happen the second time a rule is broken.

5. Ask if the parents have any questions regarding the use of consequences in the individualized plan.

6. Now, explain the positive recognition you will give the student when he or she behaves appropriately. Reiterate the importance of reinforcing the student's efforts with consistent praise and other forms of recognition. Let the parents know that you are genuinely committed to the child's success.

7. Tell the parents that you will provide a regular update to keep them informed of their child's progress. (In most cases, since parent contact will be part of the revised hierarchy, parents will hear if there's a problem. However, it's just as important to give a call or send a note when the student does behave appropriately.) Emphasize the importance of parents following through at home with positive reinforcement of their own. If appropriate, give parents a copy of the student's individualized behavior plan.

> Note: It is important that an individualized behavior plan be handled with sensitivity and caring. This is not a punitive effort; it is a plan tailor made to meet a particular student's needs. Parents need to understand that this is a positive and proactive step, the goal of which is to help their child reach his or her potential. Let your words and attitude communicate this goal.

It's Your Turn

Use the Individualized Behavior Plan form on page 121 to help prepare and record a student's individualized plan.

The individualized behavior plan should be presented to the student in a firm but empathetic manner. Difficult students need your assurance that you care, that you are there to help and that the disruptive behavior is not in their best interests.

INDIVIDUALIZED BEHAVIOR PLAN

Student's name _____ Date _____

These are the rules that _____ is expected to follow as part of this Individualized Behavior Plan:

_____

_____

_____

These are the consequences _____ will choose to receive if he/she does not comply with the rules:

   First disruption: _____

   Second disruption: _____

This is the positive recognition _____ will receive when he/she behaves appropriately.

_____

_____

_____

_____

_____

Teacher's signature   Date

Notes or comments:

_____

_____

_____

_____

_____

_____

_____

_____

_____

_____

_____

Getting the Support You Need from Parents and Administrators

In Section One you learned the importance of sharing your discipline plan with parents and with your administrator. These are important proactive measures that will help ensure that you get their support when you need it.

Keep these additional guidelines in mind as the year progresses and as behavior problems arise:

When a problem arises, take steps to deal with it on your own before asking for help.

Whenever appropriate, you should attempt to handle a student's disruptive behavior on your own before you speak to the parents or administrator about the situation. Both will want to know what actions you have taken to help the student. Assure them that you have already attempted to solve the problem on your own.

Remember, your goal is to teach the student to make good behavioral choices. If you involve parents or the administrator too soon, you are not allowing the student the opportunity to change his or her own behavior.

Document a student's behavior and the steps you have taken to handle it.

Whenever you do contact parents or an administrator about a problem, you will need accurate anecdotal documentation detailing when the problem has occurred and what steps you have taken to deal with it. Documentation strengthens your position as a professional and communicates clearly to parents that these problems do exist.

Your anecdotal record should include the following information:

- Student's name
- Date, time and place of incident
- Description of the problem
- Actions taken by the teacher.

For example:

> Name: Austin Hathaway
>
> Date: 4/24/92
>
> Problem: During math, Austin twice grabbed Allison's paper from her.
>
> Actions taken: Moved Austin to the front of the classroom for the period.

Keep these guidelines in mind when documenting problems:

Be specific. Keep away from vague opinions. Your statements should be based on factual, observable data.

Be consistent. Document problems each time they occur. Repeated occurrences may show a pattern and be helpful in solving the problem.

It's Your Turn

Use the reproducible documentation cards on page 123 to record anecdotal data about a student's behavior. Consider duplicating the cards on index stock for added durability. Fold in half with name facing forward.

Behavior Documentation Cards

Student _____ Phone # _____

Parent's Name _____ Work # _____

Parent's Name _____ Work # _____

•Date _____ Time _____ Place _____

Description of Problem/Incident: _____

_____

Action Taken: _____

_____

•Date _____ Time _____ Place _____

Description of Problem/Incident: _____

_____

Action Taken: _____

< fold here >

•Date _____ Time _____ Place _____

Description of Problem/Incident: _____

_____

Action Taken: _____

_____

•Date _____ Time _____ Place _____

Description of Problem/Incident: _____

_____

Action Taken: _____

Student _____ Phone # _____

Parent's Name _____ Work # _____

Parent's Name _____ Work # _____

•Date _____ Time _____ Place _____

Description of Problem/Incident: _____

_____

Action Taken: _____

_____

•Date _____ Time _____ Place _____

Description of Problem/Incident: _____

_____

Action Taken: _____

< fold here >

•Date _____ Time _____ Place _____

Description of Problem/Incident: _____

_____

Action Taken: _____

_____

•Date _____ Time _____ Place _____

Description of Problem/Incident: _____

_____

Action Taken: _____

Getting Support from Parents When a Problem Arises

How do you know when you should contact a parent about a problem? Some situations are very clear: severe fighting, extreme emotional distress, a student who refuses to work or turn in homework. Don't think twice about involving parents when these situations occur.

What about the day to day instances that may not be so obvious? If you are uncertain about contacting a parent, use the "Your Own Child" test. This test will put you in the position of the parent, and help clarify whether or not parental help is called for.

The "Your Own Child" Test

1. Assume you have a child of your own the same age as the student in question.

2. If your child was having the same problem in school as that student has, would you want to be called?

3. If the answer is yes, call the parent. If the answer is no, do not call the parent.

Before you pick up a phone or meet with parents, you need to outline what you are going to say. These notes will help you think through and clarify the points you want to make. Having the notes in front of you while you're speaking will help you communicate more effectively.

It's Your Turn

Assertive Discipline Cue Card #12 lists all the points you'll want to cover when contacting a parent about a problem. Reproduce and laminate this Cue Card and keep it available for reference. Use the reproducible planning sheet on page 125 to help both prepare for your meeting and to record pertinent data from the meeting.

ASSERTIVE DISCIPLINE in Action!

Contacting Parents About a Problem

Follow these steps when contacting a parent about a problem:

1 Begin with a statement of concern.

Let the parent know that you care about the student .

2 Describe the specific problem and present pertinent documentation.

Explain in specific, observable terms what the student did.

3 Describe what you have done.

Explain exactly how you have dealt with the problem so far. Make sure that the parent is aware of the steps you have already taken to solve the problem.

4 Get parental input on the problem.

Listen carefully to what the parent has to say. Here are some questions you may want to ask:

"Has your child had similar problems in the past?"

"Why do you feel your child is having these problems at school?"

"Is there something (divorce, separation, siblings, a move) going on at home that could be affecting your child's behavior?"

5 Get parental input on how to solve the problem.

Parents may have a good idea that could help solve a specific problem. Ask for input, and listen carefully to the responses.

6 Tell the parent what you will do to help solve the problem.

You've already explained what you have previously done. Let the parent know exactly what specific actions you are going to take now.

7 Explain what you need the parent to do to solve the problem.

Clearly and carefully explain specifically what you would like the parent to do.

8 Let the parent know you are confident that the problem can be worked out.

Wrap up the conversation or meeting on a positive note.

9 Tell the parent that there will be follow-up contact from you.

The parent needs to know that you are going to stay involved. Provide this reassurance by giving a specific date for a follow-up call or note.

10 Recap the conference.

Clarify all agreements. Restate and write down what you are going to do and what the parent is going to do. Keep this information in your files.

CUE CARD # 12

PARENT CONTACT WORKSHEET

Guidelines for an initial phone call or conversation about a problem

Student's name _____ Date of call or meeting _____

Parent or guardian _____

Home phone # _____ Work phone # _____

In the spaces below write the important points you will cover with the parents, and points made during the meeting or conversation.

1. Begin with a statement of concern. _____

_____

2. Describe the specific problem (state in observable terms). _____

_____

3. Review what you have already done to solve the problem. _____

_____

4. Get parental input on how to solve the problem. Record parent comments. _____

_____

5. Present your solutions to the problem.

What you will do: _____

_____

What you want the parent to do: _____

_____

6. Express confidence once again in your ability to solve the problem.

7. Arrange for follow-up contact.

Notes _____

_____

_____

_____

NOTES:

NOTES: